BASIC BEEKEEPING

Answers all the questions which a beginner might ask about the fascinating pursuit of beekeeping. The emphasis throughout is on setting up an apiary as cheaply as possible.

BASIC BEEKEEPING

Everything a Beginner Should
Know to Ensure Honey from Home

by
Owen Meyer

THORSONS PUBLISHERS LIMITED
Wellingborough, Northamptonshire

First published 1978
Second Impression 1979

ISBN 0 7225 0477 2 (paperback)
ISBN 0 7225 0488 8 (hardback)

Photoset by Specialised Offset Services Limited, Liverpool
and printed in Great Britain by
Weatherby Woolnough, Wellingborough, Northamptonshire
on paper made from 100% re-cycled fibre supplied by
P.F. Bingham Limited, Croydon, Surrey

CONTENTS

To Meg, whose tolerance and forebearance
made it possible.

INTRODUCTION

The search for self-sufficiency must surely contain an enquiry into the possibility of gathering for oneself the sweets and sugars that nature provides so abundantly – and free for the taking. After all, it is only within the recent historical past that imported sugar has been available for retail sale in Europe in any appreciable quantity. Before this, man had to rely on the natural resources of his environment. In temperate Europe large-scale cultivation of sugar beet and the development of refining processes have altered the picture, of course.

The purpose of this book is to show how an old craft, improved by modern techniques, has acquired a new lease of life to provide those who practise it with a worthwhile – and sometimes an astonishing – yield of honey. And this is quite apart from the satisfaction to be had from the successful practice of beekeeping. It is not difficult to master and there is a marked degree of comradeship and mutual help between beekeepers.

It is worth while posing a few questions.

Is beekeeping for me?

Can I do it single handed or do I need help?

If so, where can I get that help?

Can I keep bees in my own garden?

Are the circumstances of my house, soil, normal weather, proximity of neighbours, factors to be considered?

What equipment do I need?

What is the cost (a) initially? (b) upkeep and renewals?

Are there different strains of bees?

How do I start?

What kind of crop can I expect?

Can I dispose of any surplus?

The aim of this book is to answer these questions and also to give an introduction to bees and beekeeping generally. Most people, having started, find the subject is so absorbing and has so many fascinating avenues to explore that they want to go into the questions posed more deeply.

This book is intended for the beginner to beekeeping and as you progress you may want to read about the subject in more depth. There are books which go into this in detail, but be wary of titles more than fifty years old which have not been revised. Join other beekeepers in their local associations and clubs. There is a vast reservoir of accumulated expertise which is never published but which will be willingly passed on.

Much of the equipment the beginner will need is expensive if bought new so I have suggested ways of improvising and of making many items yourself. In doing so, I have assumed only a modest ability to use simple tools and to work accurately to measurements. There is much to be said for the do-it-yourself approach. To make any sort of apparatus, however simple, involves understanding the basic principles. For the same reason, I have included a section on the natural history of the honeybee. I am quite sure that to keep any form of stock successfully it is necessary to have a good idea of 'what makes them tick'.

1
THE BACKGROUND TO BEEKEEPING

Although man has profited from honeybees for many centuries, the bees themselves have never been tamed or domesticated in any way. In form they have remained almost unchanged since prehistoric times. The best that we have been able to do is to breed by selection from strains of local bees in an effort to maintain and increase those characteristics we think desirable. The bees in the beekeepers' hives are exactly the same physically as the many wild colonies in hollow trees and similar sites. There are very many such sites for the swarm, which, as we shall see later, is the natural form of colony reproduction, sends its scouts out to look for a place which will provide shelter from wind and rain, and have an upper surface from which a comb can be built, space below in which it can hang, and an entrance small enough to be defended against intruders. Hollow trees, roof spaces, wall cavities and church steeples all satisfy these requirements.

Primitive man soon discovered that he liked the sweet taste of honey and the wild colonies were robbed by honey hunters. This primitive 'beekeeping' is still practised by less developed communities throughout the world and the honeycomb, complete with honey, pollen and larvae, is eagerly devoured, providing a very useful addition of both carbohydrate and protein to what may otherwise be a poor and monotonous diet.

As man became more pastoral and less nomadic the need arose to establish a more permanent home for his bees, which would be more conveniently to hand than the wild colonies and which could be clearly identified as his own. So the idea of a hive came about.

Bees are able to collect natural food in excess of their current needs in good times (summer) and store it in a form in which it will not deteriorate for many, many years for use in times of dearth. As we shall see, the colony can regenerate all its members – even the queen – who are replaced by natural processes when they become inefficient through age, disease or accident.

Primitive man found that a swarm could easily be induced to settle down in a receptacle into which it was introduced and, barring accidents, would go on from year to year giving him honey, providing he was not too greedy and did not rob his bees of their food stores for the long, cold winter. We are here considering Europe, although very similar conditions apply to tropical regions.

It is worth noticing these simple facts because it is on them that the whole basis of modern beekeeping depends, despite the frills and additions so beloved of mankind.

Early Hives
Through the ages, man quite naturally used the materials that were to hand for his hives – and still does. In a forest area he used the bark of trees or hollow logs, and with the advent of tools, sawn planks of timber were an obvious improvement. An agricultural group would use coiled straw sewn together with strands of split bracken for the familiar straw skeps or hives made from woven wickerwork and plastered with cow dung for strength or weather-proofing. In parts of the Middle East, where timber is scarce, earthenware containers in the form of pots or pipes would find favour. All these methods are in current use in various parts of the globe. All have their advantages – and some disadvantages too.

In the twentieth century, with a world shortage of timber and rocketing prices, we are experimenting, with varying degrees of success, with man-made materials – marine plywood, fibre glass, expanded polystyrene and other petro-chemical derivatives – but it is doubtful if we have yet found a satisfactory substitute for sawn and prepared planks of sound matured timber, assuming that one can find the money for it!

In nearly all the primitive types of hive the combs would be attached to the upper surface and walls inside the container so that it was difficult to remove honey without some disturbance to the bees unless they were first killed, and this was, in fact, quite a common method. Up to quite recent times, bees were killed at the end of the summer by placing the skep over a shallow pit of burning sulphur. Thus the honeycomb was free of bees.

A less wasteful and more humane method was 'driving' the bees off their combs. The skep to be cleared would be heavily smoked and inverted. Over the top would be put an empty skep of similar size with a band of cloth secured round the outside with iron pins. Rhythmic drumming on the sides of the lower (occupied) skep with the palms of the hands or short wooden staves would cause the bees to leave their combs and march up into the empty skep. The bees could then be united to a weak lot, left to draw new comb (if driven early enough in the year), or returned to their original skep after some of the honeycomb had been removed. If performed by a competent beekeeper, this was quite a spectacular performance and one which was a common item in demonstrations at county agricultural shows and honey shows.

The Greeks, as they did with so many other problems, invented a way out. They would set their conical wicker hives upside down – with the mouth of the basket upwards. Sticks or slats of wood were laid across the open mouth, and if the spacing was right, the bees would build their combs down from the sticks and would not attach them to the sides. Some kind of covering against light and weather completed the set-up. Individual combs could then be withdrawn.

Some Milestones in the Development of Modern Beekeeping

In 1851 an American beekeeper, Langstroth, observed that bees would 'respect' a space of about $\frac{3}{8}$ inch (9mm). This simple discovery revolutionized beekeeping and is the underlying principle of hive construction to this day. It simply means that if a rectangular box-like hive is constructed with some means of suspending rectangular frames so that there is always a gap of $\frac{3}{8}$ inch (9mm) between the outside of the frames and the inner surface of the walls and similarly between the tops of the frames and the bottom of any frames in boxes placed above, then the bees would readily pass round the frame ends and over the tops. If the gap is less than $\frac{1}{4}$ inch (6mm) the bees will glue the frames to the hive walls using propolis, a resinous substance collected from trees and plants. If the gap is more than $\frac{3}{8}$ inch (9mm) the bees will bridge it with brace comb (irregular honeycomb made of beeswax).

In 1857 in Holland, Mehring cast thin sheets of beeswax between moulds bearing the impression of the bases of cells. The insertion of these into frames saves the bees a great deal of time and labour, giving them a good start and help in the production of straight combs. In 1876 A.I. Root in the U.S.A. improved the method of manufacture by using a metal roller press. This is the modern method and beekeeping appliance manufacturers offer such sheets, called foundation, reinforced with crimped wire for strength. There are efficient ways of producing foundation at home using wax and simple hand presses.

It was thought desirable that the bees should be persuaded to store their honey in separate boxes and at the same time prevent the queen from having access to them. The removal of a honey surplus would be facilitated and it would be stored in combs used for no other purpose. This was accomplished by placing a queen excluder over the brood nest (the box in which the queen has free access for egg-laying and brood rearing). This is a screen either of slotted zinc or parallel stiff wires spaced so that the workers can pass through the slots or the spaces but the queen cannot because of her larger abdomen. Further boxes can then be placed over the queen excluder as needed. These are called 'supers'. At the end of the summer bees can be removed from the supers (see 'Taking the Crop' page 35), the honey extracted and the combs kept for future use. With care the only damage to the combs will be the removal of the cappings in order to open the cells.

2
WHAT YOU NEED TO START

Many people who would like to start beekeeping in a modest way are deterred by the high cost of the equipment involved, and certainly the high cost of good quality timber or of labour in what is a comparatively small market have meant that prices of professionally made beekeeping equipment have risen step by step with inflation — but then so has the price of a pound of honey. The ordinary man or woman who can use his or her hands and simple tools can make many of the items described in this section and I have tried to indicate where good serviceable things can be made or improvised at a fraction of the cost of the professionally made article. Do not forget that well-made equipment will last many years with a modicum of care. Many beekeepers are using hives that are forty or more years old. Providing they are made well, accurately and of sound materials, they will last.

Hives
Of all the controversies between beekeepers, the subject of hive design has, I think, generated the most heat and acrimony. I do not propose to add to it here. It has always seemed to me that bees will live quite happily in any sort of cavity from a hollow tree to the most carefully planned and elaborate modern hive constructed of man-made materials with all the latest gadgetry. Of course, they will do better in some because of heat insulation, ventilation, dryness and other factors, but the overriding consideration is always which hive type is the easiest for the amateur to make and to get bits and pieces for.

For simplicity I think we must opt for a single-walled hive. Double-walled hives (W.B.C.) are undoubtedly more attractive in appearance and better for ventilation (often because the inner boxes fit so badly that gaps and crevices abound) but they are extravagant in the use of

W.B.C. hive.

W.B.C. hive showing inner boxes.

timber, more complicated to make, and difficult to move when occupied by bees.

Of the single-walled hives, the Smith pattern is the easiest to make. It consists of four boards joined to make a box, open at top and bottom, with rebates formed in opposite faces on the inside so that the frame lugs can rest in these rebates.

Because of the shallowness of the rebates the lugs have to be short. ($\frac{3}{4}$ inch (19mm) compared with $1\frac{1}{2}$ inches (38mm) for the Standard British frames). The short lugs do not give quite enough to grip and the beginner, especially if wearing gloves, can find them a little difficult to handle smoothly. The hive holds eleven standard frames (standard, that is, apart from the shortened lugs) and is rectangular in plan. Internal dimensions are $16\frac{1}{4}$ inches (420mm) by $14\frac{5}{8}$ inches (371mm). Handgrips are formed by scooping out fingergrips in the side walls − not a very good handhold for a full brood box − and a weakening of the side walls.

The Modified National hive also takes eleven British Standard frames but is $18\frac{1}{8}$ inches (460mm) square externally. 'Rails' are formed by building shallow boxes out from opposite sides to accommodate the frame lugs. These external additions make good firm hand holds. More National hives are in use in the United Kingdom than any other design and their popularity is growing. It is eminently suitable for home construction and its square section leads to ease of manipulation and adaptability. It is also easy to transport. It is not so handsome as the W.B.C. and has been criticized on the grounds that eleven British Standard frames are not sufficient for a prolific queen. The answer is, of course, to use bees of a local strain which are not so prolific and are more frugal or, if necessary, to practise a double brood-chamber system as outlined in Chapter 3.

The Langstroth hive is a single-walled hive of simple construction rather similar to the Smith but taking larger frames. It is the hive in common use in Continental Europe, the USA and Australia.

Comparisons of the surface areas of comb available in the brood chamber of these hives are:

W.B.C.	2040 sq.in. (12,444 sq.cm)
National	2244 sq.in. (14,586 sq.cm)
Smith	2244 sq.in. (14,586 sq.cm)
Langstroth	2740 sq.in. (17,810 sq.cm)

National and W.B.C. hives have bottom bee space; that is, the tops of the frames are level with the top of the hive body. The Smith and Langstroth has top bee space — the tops of the frames hang so that they are a bee space — $\frac{1}{4}$ inch (6mm) — below the top of the hive body. Top or bottom bee space is another fruitful source of fierce wrangling among beekeepers.

I have seen no conclusive scientific evidence to indicate that bees are any healthier in one or other type of hive so it is very much a question of personal preference. However, whatever type of hive you decide is the best for you — stick to it. There is nothing more frustrating than having two or three types of hive in an apiary so that nothing is interchangeable.

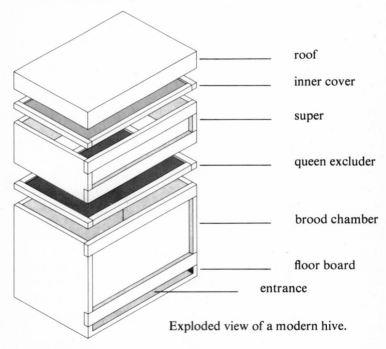

roof

inner cover

super

queen excluder

brood chamber

floor board

entrance

Exploded view of a modern hive.

The four types of hives discussed (and there are others) are stocked by the appliance manufacturers, both made up and 'in the flat' (kits of parts ready machined for home assembly).

They can also be made at home or at woodwork classes at Evening Institutes quite easily. Working drawings of the W.B.C., Smith and Modified National can be had from the British Beekeepers Association (see page 94). Internal dimensions and clearances must be adhered to strictly otherwise you will have problems. As for materials, prime Western Red Cedar is the best but it is expensive and is becoming scarce, particularly in the widths needed. It needs no preservative and is easy to work but is, I think, too soft. Deal is satisfactory but needs a wood preservative; grades of Cuprinol and Solignum are suitable if they contain no insecticide. Deal is heavier than cedar.

However, I am not at all sure that we need be confined to timber boards. Some grades of chipboard are bounded with water-resistant resin. I have made and used Modified National hives of this material for some time without any bad effects at all. It is considerably heavier than cedar but does not warp. A $\frac{1}{4}$-inch (6mm) bee space remains at $\frac{1}{4}$-inch (6mm) after two years' use and this is more than can be said of many professionally made hives. Do not be afraid to experiment with such materials (perhaps offcuts) as come your way. Sound floorboards from a demolished building are a possibility too, but remember that it is the internal dimensions that are important.

Supers

Whichever type of hive you decide upon, the complete set of parts you will need will be a floor with an entrance block; a deep ($8\frac{7}{8}$ inch or 21cm) box for a brood chamber in which the queen will lay her eggs and the nurse bees raise them to adulthood; an inner cover; and a roof.

As spring and summer advance you will need to add a queen excluder (see page 22) to confine the queen to the brood chamber and to place 'supers' – sometimes called 'shallows' – on top of this. These are boxes made to the same specifications as the deep brood box except that the supers are only $5\frac{7}{8}$ inches (149mm) deep. In other respects they are similar.

The reason for using shallow boxes (and consequently shallower frames) is simply one of convenience of handling. The total weight of a shallow super with eleven combs full of honey may be nearly 30 lb (13.5kg) – quite enough for most people to manhandle. To increase the depth to the normal brood size would increase the weight too much for comfort.

I imagine that supers are so called because they are superimposed above the brood chamber. Their main function is to provide space in which the bees can process nectar and store honey but a secondary, and most important, use is to provide much needed 'parking space' for the bees when the colony is populous and thus avoid overcrowding below.

There is nothing quite so frustrating as being caught short of supers when your bees are working a good nectar flow and your only super is solid with honey, so as soon as you can, it is a good idea to make a few spare supers so that you have three for each hive. If you *are* caught with no spare supers it is always possible to extract a few combs, adding them back to the supers from which they came immediately. Be quick about this and get the whole job done in an evening if you possibly can. To leave spaces in the hive will only encourage the bees to build wild comb.

Frames
The bees will build their wax combs in the hanging frames which the beekeeper fits in his hives. The frames are rectangular and designed to leave a bee space all round. Lugs are formed by extensions of the top bars so that the frames can be hung from the rebates in the side walls of the hive or from the built-out portions of the hive. Sheets of wax foundation, strengthened with fine wire inserts, are fixed in the frames in grooves machined in the inner faces of the side bars and the wedge in the top bar.

Construction has to be accurate in order to maintain the bee spaces of 3/16-5/16 inch (5-8mm) and it is best to buy these from the manufacturers, at least in the early stages of your beekeeping.

The design of the frames and the hive will ensure the proper spacing round the sides, top and bottom of the frames, but they must also be spaced relatively to each other. This is done in one of two ways:

(a) By using self-spacing ('Hoffman') frames. These have projecting shoulders on the side bars, alternately square and chamfered so that when they are pressed firmly together the required centre to centre distance is automatically achieved.

(b) By using metal or plastic 'spacers' either in the form of small boxes which fit over the lugs or of metal clips which fit over the side bars to form shoulders to bear on similar shoulders on neighbouring frames (Yorkshire spacers). In both cases, pressing together again gives the right spacing.

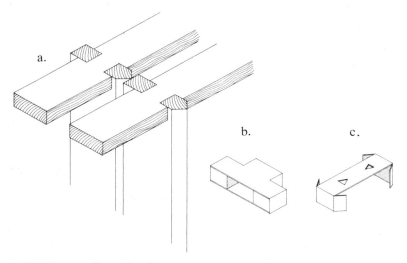

a. Hoffman self-spacing frames.
b. Metal end.
c. Yorkshire spacer.

Personal Protection

It is often possible to handle bees without any protection at all but it is foolish to do so, especially for a beginner. A hat with a wide brim and a netting veil will look after you from the neck up. The appliance manufacturers sell veils and combined hats and veils which are excellent in every way. Such items and others are regularly advertised in the bee journals (see page 93). However, a serviceable veil can be made from nylon net for a few pence. Get black nylon because it is much easier to see through than a light colour. Make a tube of the netting a little less than the width of your shoulders. Hem one end of the tube and insert a length of elastic so that it grips the crown of your hat tightly.

For a hat, a ladies' straw or a school boater (called a 'biff' in some parts) will serve admirably. The essentials are lightness and a brim to keep the net off your face. An added refinement could be a ring of wire sewn to the veil at about mouth level. This will prevent the veil resting on the back of your neck.

When using the hat, tuck the open end of the veil inside your jacket and button up. If you like to work in shirtsleeves, and many do, sew the middle of a length of tape to the bottom edge of the back part of the veil. Pass the ends round under the arms and tie in a bow on your chest over the front of the veil.

Gloves

Fine leather gloves with linen gauntlets can be bought but again it is much cheaper to improvise. Thin rubber washing-up gloves are not much use but there are gloves on the market made of a rubbery substance on a cloth basis which are slightly bumpy on the outside. Gauntlets long enough to reach up the arms nearly to the elbow can be sewn on. Elasticate the top (open) ends so that they stay in place. There is a good deal of snobbery about the use of gloves. If the added protection gives you confidence, use them. You will probably find that in time and in good weather conditions you will discard them but keep them handy. There comes a time for all of us when, for one reason or another, a job with the bees has to be completed and they are not too amenable. The wise use gloves; the brash stick it out and then boast about the number of stings they had. Some beekeepers like to use short cuffs elasticated at both ends. These are worn between the wrists and the cuffs of the shirt to prevent bees crawling up.

Legs

Bees have the instinct to climb and to seek dark places. It is a little disconcerting to find yourself holding a frame of bees and to feel one or more of your little friends steadily climbing up inside a trouser leg. The answer is to tuck your trousers into wellingtons or your socks. Wellingtons are better; some bees seem to be attracted to socks, especially if they are woollen. For obvious reasons, jeans or trousers are advisable for ladies when manipulating their bees.

One type of veil, fitted to a plastic helmet. The lower ring keeps the veil well away from the face and elastic loops pass under the arms to hold the veil down on the shoulders.

Ready for the worst: veil, trousers tucked into Wellington boots, leather gloves with cotton gauntlets attached reaching to elbows.

Hive Tool

This is a metal tool for levering apart frames before lifting them. You will find that your bees will stick everything together with propolis. Very nice hive tools of different designs are sold, but why not use an old long-handled screwdriver or, by a simple bit of blacksmithing, heat and beat out the end of an old flat metal file, which has come to the end of its useful life, into a blunt chisel edge? Heat the tang and when cherry red bend it round on itself to form a U. This makes a good hook for easing out a well stuck-down frame.

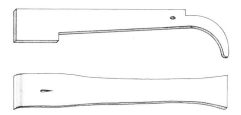

Two types of hive tool.

Queen Excluder

A queen excluder will be needed for each hive you have. These are sheets of zinc or plastic the exact size of the hive perforated with slots just wide enough to allow the passage of the workers but too narrow to let the queen through. Another type is a grid of wires similarly spaced. I prefer them framed with $\frac{1}{4}$-inch (6mm) timber but have to be careful which way up I use them. On hives where the frame tops are flush with the top of the hive body, such as the National (bottom bee space), the framing should be on the underside of the excluder as installed so that there is the required bee space between the tops of the frames and the excluder. Queen excluders do not lend themselves to home construction, because they need to be made very accurately.

Queen excluder: zinc 'long slot' type.

Smokers

These consist of a fire box into which smouldering material is placed burning side downwards. Bees are afraid of fire, so will gorge themselves with honey which makes them slow and less likely to sting.

A bellows drives air through a hole towards the bottom of the fire box with the result that a stream of smoke comes out of a nozzle in the lid. Get a good-sized smoker – or make one yourself. Design is of little importance once the principles are grasped. Although I am probably the world's worse tinsmith I managed to make a useful smoker out of an odd sheet of copper I unearthed in that household necessity, a 'junk' box. I was unable to make the lid fit perfectly so that, in use, my smoker puffs quite as much smoke over me as it does over the bees. This is an eminently satisfactory arrangement. It discourages me from being heavy handed with smoke, which is a good thing, and provides much innocent amusement for my critical beekeeping friends.

I used rivets and soft solder for the seams and although the experts, with much wise wagging of heads, assured me that the heat of the firebox would melt the solder and that I should have used hard solder. Even after many years' use this has not happened – so far. Either they keep their smokers going too fiercely or I keep mine going not fiercely enough. Rotten wood when dry, old sacking and rolls of corrugated cardboard (but not the fireproof kind) all make good fuels.

Smoker.

Very very occasionally it may be necessary to anaesthetize bees. One common way of doing this is to use a dried puff ball as a smoker fuel. This is a fungus producing large fruiting bodies like khaki coloured footballs. When dried and used in the smoker it anaesthetizes the bees but tends to make them fall off the combs. Another method is to soak a few rolls of corrugated cardboard in a solution of saltpetre and then dry them. When using, light the roll and insert it in your smoker with the lighted end at the top – the reverse of the usual way – otherwise you will have a firework in your hands. Chloroform and ether have been used but these are best left well alone. They are dangerous chemicals anyway and should have no place in the beekeeper's shed. If you decide to keep a saltpetre roll handy for an emergency, mark it in red ink so that you cannot use it by mistake, and remember that anaesthetized bees can often be very fractious after recovery.

Feeders

It is best to have a feeder for each hive. Two types of feeder are in common use. A rapid feeder consists of a cylindrical vessel (usually of metal) with a lid and a central tube up which the bees can crawl. The vessel is filled with sugar solution and placed over the feed hole. A tube slightly larger than the central access tube, often with a glass top, is inverted over the central tube. This prevents the bees coming up through the central tube in large numbers and drowning themselves – which they will do unless prevented.

Feeders can be made easily from any suitably sized tin such as a Dundee cake tin. A short length of $\frac{3}{4}$-inch (19mm) copper pipe makes a satisfactory central tube. I find it easiest to solder the tube inside the tin before cutting an access hole.

The quickest feeder of all, and perhaps the easiest to make, is the 'Ashforth' type. This is a wooden tray some 3 or 4 inches (76-101mm) deep and of the same dimensions as the hive with some kind of 'up and over' trap on one side. A gallon or so of syrup can be given in such a feeder, as against the pint or so in the metal type.

Contact feeders are sometimes useful. Punch a few very small holes with a sharp bradawl in a 1 inch (25mm) circle in the lid of a lever-lid tin of good size. Fill the tin with sugar syrup and replace the lid firmly – it must be a good tight fit. Invert over the feed hole, or even directly

Rapid feeder: parts displayed.

on to the frames. A few drops will come out but no more. Air pressure outside and the partial vacuum inside will prevent leakage, and the bees can take the sugar syrup through the holes as and when they want it.

Excellent feeders of all types can, of course, be had from the Appliance Manufacturers. They are very efficient and handsome, but cost more than your home-made kinds, and I do not believe that the bees will notice the difference.

Extractor

An extractor will be needed when taking the crop (see page 35). This is an expensive item and eventually you will want to have your own. Until then, you will find that most Beekeeping Associations have an extractor which they will hire out to members for a nominal fee. An extractor *can* be made by the determined D.I.Y. enthusiast and I have a dedicated friend who has done just this. His contraption is made from an old milk churn. The inside frame-holding cage is a bird cage and the handle and gearing for the drive started life as part of a hand sheep-shearer.

Strainer

Before storing, your honey should be strained and allowed to settle. I find that it is best to buy a strainer. They are made of either perforated zinc or wire mesh, rather like a large domestic gravy strainer, and their purpose is to hold back the bits of beeswax which will inevitably become detached during the uncapping process. After the initial straining, I like to run my honey through something finer. A new nylon stocking will do but I prefer a nylon bag as used by amateur wine makers. This will remove all the tiny bits which have got through the strainer and will give a nice 'bright' honey.

Settling Vessel

The extractor will whirl the combs round so fast that myriads of air bubbles will be driven into the honey. After straining, run the honey into a tank of good size – big enough to hold 100 lb (45kg). Special

Extractor (right), small settling tank (left) and
cone-shaped perforated zinc strainer (between).

settling tanks are sold (they used to be called 'ripeners' for some reason which has always escaped me), but any large container will do, providing it has a well-fitting lid and a bottom tap. Try the fermentation vessel you use for your home-made beer or wine. Leave in a warm place for at least twenty-four hours — forty-eight is better. The object is to allow the bubbles to rise to the top. A bottom tap will allow you to draw off the cleared honey from the bottom. If your settling vessel has no bottom tap you will have to scoop off the froth with a large spoon and then ladle the honey out.

Storage Tins

You will probably want to try your new season's honey as soon as possible, so fill a few jars straight away. However, you will find it more convenient to store the bulk in 28 lb (12kg) containers. A friendly baker may be persuaded to let you have a few of the large tins his fondant arrives in. These are ideal and cheap. The best kind have lever lids but nowadays most have a rimmed lid which fits over the tin. After filling and replacing the lid, run a length of wide sellotape round the edge of the lid to make things airtight. Honey is very hygroscopic — that is, it has a great affinity for water, which it will absorb from the air if allowed to. Always try to prevent this happening by not leaving bulk honey exposed a moment longer than necessary. If you cannot get cheap tins, you can buy plastic buckets with clip-on lids which are very good for the job.

Containers of any kind must be scrupulously clean inside and out. Any sign of rust spots inside metal tins renders them unsuitable for our purpose but all is not lost. Where small patches of plating have gone and rust has appeared the tins can still be used. Clean off the rust spots as thoroughly as you can and line the tin with a polythene bag taller and wider than the tin. Fill the bag with honey to within an inch or so of the top of the tin and seal with a paper/wire binder as used for freezer bags. The tin will give rigidity and strength and the polythene will keep the honey away from the corroded plating.

Store the filled and sealed tins in a cool place and your honey will keep in perfect condition until you want to bottle it later on. It may — probably will — crystallize. If it does, you will have the choice of 'thick' or 'thin' — clear-run honey or crystallized. When it crystallizes, honey undergoes no chemical change. It simply means the extracted honey, being an oversaturated solution of sugars in water, is unstable physically and will nearly always crystallize out, but not always evenly. Crystallized honey can always be turned back into clear-run by warming it gently – never at more than 140°F (60°C) and preferably at 120°F (49°C) – for the shortest time required to clear it. Excessive heating drives off the volatile flower essences and aromatic oils which give your honey its aroma and flavour. It can then be run off into bottles. It is worth while using the standard glass jars with screw tops and waxed card wads sold for honey. Indeed, you must do so if you intend to sell any honey.

Creaming Honey

If you want creamed honey, warm the tin gently until the honey is soft enough to move but is not liquified. Now agitate it to break up the mass into the consistency of firm cream. There are a number of ways of doing this and tools can be improvised. A long wooden spoon will do but few are long enough to reach the bottom of a 28 lb (12kg) tin.

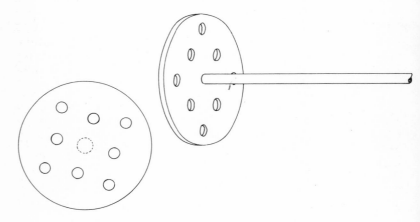

A simple creaming device made from a metal disc
and a wooden rod.

A metal disc 2 inches (5cm) less than the diameter of the tin with a number of $\frac{1}{2}$-inch (12mm) holes can be screwed to the end of a stout wooden rod (two screws to prevent the disc moving on the rod) and the disc pressed down carefully through the soft honey and then up and down until creaming has been completed. A domestic food mixer will deal with small quantities at a time. I use a paint paddle, kept for this purpose only, fitted in the chuck of an electric hand drill and I find it works well. Remember not to switch on until the paddle is completely immersed in the honey and to switch off before it is taken out. I once leant over to switch on the light while doing this and the spinning paddle momentarily broke surface. The resultant spray of honey did nothing at all to increase my popularity in the family! A little honey, if spread thinly, can be made to cover a very wide area indeed.

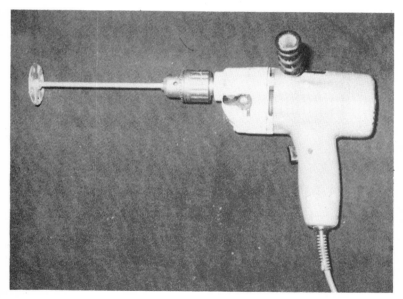

Creamer, made from a paint paddle and kept specially for honey, attached to an electric hand drill.

3

THE BEEKEEPER'S YEAR

It is usually said that the beekeeper's year starts with autumn preparations for wintering, and it is true that the success of a colony during the following summer is made or marred to a large extent on what the beekeeper has done, or forgotten to do, during the previous autumn. However, May is a good time to start beekeeping so let us start our review of the year a little before then.

Try to have your new bees delivered from late April to mid May. During the winter you will have been reading all the books you have been able to get hold of and, if you are wise, joined your local Beekeeping Association. During the winter months these associations meet for talks on beekeeping subjects and always have their quota of people who are experienced and happy to pass on practical advice and help to the tyro.

What Type of Bees?
It is a good plan to acquire your first bees through an association. There is no doubt in my mind that the 'best' bee is likely to be a local bee of known characteristics and temperament. Insist on a good-tempered strain. If you live, say, in the Midlands, bees which have been bred for generations and established themselves there are more likely to do well with you than bees from the North or from southern counties where there will be entirely different environments as to flora and prevailing weather. They will have become acclimatized to these and so do well in them.

Knowledgeable beekeepers will tell you of the superb results they get with Caucasian queens of a special strain or queens imported directly from Australia, the U.S.A. or other exotic parts. These claims are not usually exaggerated but experimental breeding is not for the beginner. Later on, when you feel more confident, you may try some new breeds, but start with an honest-to-goodness local bee of tried and tested capabilities, and learn from it.

There are advantages in starting with a nucleus − a small colony of some six frames complete with young queen, eggs, brood and stores, which is a going concern though on a small scale. While waiting for your nucleus to arrive, check over all the equipment you will have got together − hive, spare frames, foundation, supers, smoker, feeder, veil and gloves.

You will have chosen the site for your hive carefully, taking advice from a local beekeeper if possible. Ideally (but not essentially), this should have a southern aspect and be sheltered from wind. A 'tunnel' situation between two buildings is not good. It *must* be in a position where the bees' flight will not be an annoyance to neighbours, children or passers-by. It would clearly be inconsiderate to have the entrance close to and facing a public right of way, for instance. It is a good idea to get your bees up to normal flying height as quickly as possible by arranging a hedge or fence or some such obstacle 5 or 6 feet (1.5-2m) high in front of the hive. Remember to arrange for working space all round the hive for yourself.

The Arrival of the Bees

Your nucleus will arrive either in a 'nucleus box' which is really no more than a half-sized hive, or a travelling box with a gauze screen for ventilation. In either case, remove the roof and brood boxes from your hive, leaving the floor exactly where you plan it should remain permanently. Place the nucleus/travelling box on the floor board of your hive with its entrance facing the way your hive entrance is to face. Remove the perforated zinc or whatever is closing the entrance hole and allow the bees to fly. Do nothing more until the evening of the next day, then gently place the nucleus box on the ground beside the hive. Have your smoker alight and wear your veil − gloves too, if you are a mite nervous about a possible (but unlikely) sting. The object is to transfer the bees to your hive with the least possible disturbance. An unexpected sting just might make the inexperienced jerk the frame he is holding; this should be avoided, especially if the queen is on it. So by all means wear gloves if you want to. As the time goes on you will probably dispense with them.

Put the deep box back on your hive floor with its entrance block inserted with the larger of the two openings in operation. Remove the lid of the nucleus/travelling box, taking care not to jerk it. Blow a very little smoke across the tops of the frames but never down between them. Gently lift each frame by the lugs and place them in your hive box in the same order and facing the same way as they were in the travelling box, starting at one side of the hive.

You will be unable to resist looking for the queen but do not prolong your search – if you cannot see her this does not mean that she is not there. Place a frame of wax foundation on either side of the frames and close them up until the shoulders abut if they are the self-spacing variety or so that the metal ends are in line and tight together. Blank off the remaining space with a division board (a piece of board the dimensions of the inside of the hive hung to a normal frame top). Replace the inner cover to the hive and give a feeder of sugar syrup, 2 lb (900g) sugar to 1 pt. (575ml) water. Try to restrain your eagerness to open up and see how things are going for a week but keep the feeder topped up at dusk. You are trying to give your colony a helping hand until it has enough foragers to look after itself. Do not be too anxious to inspect every frame until the weather is really warm but check that the foundation on the outside frames is being drawn out. Add fresh frames of foundation when the inner faces of the outside combs seem fairly full of bees.

In a good year such a colony started in April or May could well grow strong enough to give a modest surplus in the first summer. In many districts the main flow occurs in quite a short time in late July. If the colony grows well, as it should, resist the temptation to divide it in two. It is far better to finish your first summer with a strong colony in good heart with plenty of stores for itself for the winter and perhaps some surplus for you, rather than to divide it and have two 'strugglers' which have to be re-united in the autumn with doubtful prospects for the winter. A great deal will be learnt about bees during this first summer and by starting with a small nucleus, your own confidence and competence will grow as the colony grows.

Learning From Beekeepers

Spend as many Saturday afternoons as you can spare at the demonstrations organized by your local Beekeeping Association, and watch others manipulate their bees. This will give you a standard of comparison. The newcomer who lifts out a frame solid with khaki sealed brood which he put in a few weeks ago as a sheet of foundation can feel a real thrill of pride. He can now say 'These really are *my* bees'.

By the time nectar is coming in in quantity, your brood box will be full of bees and brood in all stages and you should think about giving more room in order to avoid congestion. With most strains of bee you are likely to encounter, two full-sized deep boxes often gives more room than the queen needs, but one box is not enough. One answer is to add a shallow box (called a super) over the deep one at this stage and allow the queen the run of both boxes. There is much argument over this method of having your bees on 'one and a half' boxes. Having brood on two sizes of frames can be a bother but the system has the merit of flexibility. In alternate years the boxes can be reversed in the Spring with advantages, and the whole outfit is not too heavy for most people. It is a practical compromise and if you decide to winter your bees on one box it is not difficult to get the queen down into the bottom box towards the end of the summer and keep her down with an excluder, thus leaving the top shallow box as an additional super. My own feeling is that it is better and far safer to winter the queen in a deep box with a shallow box of sealed stores above – no excluder, of course. I prefer, too, to get my honey from combs which have never been used for breeding.

Catching the Nectar Flow

In subsequent years, when you have a full-sized colony (or colonies), the great problem in May will be when to add supers to catch an early flow of nectar. Wait until six frames in the upper box contain brood and then add your queen excluder and a super. On balance it is better to be too soon than too late, but keep an eye on the weather. Early nectar flows can be fickle even if you live in a fruit area. The addition of a super of foundation or even of drawn comb will certainly cool things down and may check brood rearing if the weather turns really cool. Brood may even be deserted as the bees cluster tighter on cold nights. But leaving supering too late can cause congestion, which in turn can mean a check in brood rearing and is one of the factors leading to early swarming.

If, as suggested above, you decide to let the queen have the run of two boxes it is unlikely that you will have any swarming trouble in the first year, even if your second box is a shallow, and there should be no problem about wintering satisfactorily. Of course, your 'take' of honey will be reduced by the amount stored in the top box, but so much the better for the bees.

During June and July it is best to have no entrance block in the hive. A good strong colony needs all the ventilation it can get. If your nucleus, perhaps because of indifferent weather, has failed to build up strongly by this time — and it can happen — by all means leave the entrance block in position. A small entrance is more easily defended than a large one and helps to conserve warmth.

By observation and by talking to other beekeepers, try to find out what is the normal duration and timing of the local nectar flow. Quite often it is concentrated into a very short period in July and your aim should be to have the maximum foraging force at this time. It is impossible to lay down hard and fast rules on how to do this but by giving room and feeding in the spring much can be done to give your bees a boost. Only time and experience can guide you.

Do not be in a hurry to remove the 'surplus' stored in the super(s) in July. Early in the summer, bees may have nearly all their stores in the super and very little in the brood chamber. Give them a chance to take some down. We often get a cold spell in July too, and if you have taken their all they will be in real trouble.

Additional Swarms

During late July and early August you may be offered late swarms by beekeepers who have enough. If you can get these hived not later than, say, 15 August they will stand a fair chance of establishing themselves, building up a colony of young bees for the winter and collecting a reasonable amount of stores, especially pollen, but you may have to feed sugar syrup to augment natural stores.

Driven bees or nuclei offered after mid-August are best politely declined by the beginner. They will need heavy feeding if they are to survive the winter and even so it is a gamble. Nuclei can be — and often are — kept throughout the winter headed by a young queen, but usually by the more experienced beekeeper.

It is far better to add to your apiary earlier in the summer if the opportunity arises, if only because in his second spring the beginner will be keen to increase and may be tempted to divide his carefully nurtured, and by now strong, stock into nuclei. Resist this.Keep your original stock strong – it will repay you.

Taking the Crop

'How much should I expect?' is a normal and not unreasonable question beginners ask. The answer will depend of course on a number of factors. In the first place, the situation of the hive is of prime importance. Although it is true to say that there are very few locations in the British Isles which will not support a few colonies of bees and yield a moderate surplus, local weather tendencies, agricultural methods and soil composition will obviously all affect the final result. For instance, a predominantly fruit growing area might be expected to provide an early nectar flow – and then? What is to follow? Are there follow-up crops? Is there a fair amount of rough forage in the shape of hedgerows, common lands and so on – blackberries, Willow Herb?

A large area of cereal crops is not likely to be any good for beekeeping unless there are other sources of nectar within flying distance. All this means, of course, that observation of one's own environment is a good guide. And do not underestimate the suburban garden. Many localities have superb flowering trees, there for the working. However, taking into account all these 'ifs' and 'buts', over the years you should expect to get an average yearly surplus of 30-40 lb (14-18kg) of honey per colony after leaving a reasonable quantity in the hive for winter stores.

The end of the summer will find you with one, two, or even three supers of honey above a queen excluder on each colony (some are always 'more equal than others'). Do not be in a hurry to remove your surplus. It has been said that honey left in the comb on a hive matures and improves in flavour. I do not think there is any scientific basis for this belief but it may be true nevertheless, and the cessation of a honey flow often leaves bees rather touchy. It is also necessary to see that the nectar has been completely processed by the bees and the cells sealed so that by leaving well alone for a week or so at the end of a nectar flow the bees will be more amenable and the honey properly ripened. Your object will be to get the bees out of the supers with a minimum of disturbance to them – and consequently to you.

Three methods are available:

1. *Shake and brush.* Lift a frame from a super. Shake and/or brush off every bee and place the comb in an empty super. Keep this covered to prevent the return of the bees. The traditional tool for brushing is a flight feather from a goose wing, and the Appliance Manufacturers sell special soft brushes for the purpose. A handful of longish grass does the job just as well — and is considerably cheaper.

Brushing (1).

The shaking and brushing always creates a good deal of
excitement among the bees and can lead to robbing. It is not
recommended for the inexperienced but can be a useful way of
taking off the odd comb of sealed honey during the active season.
We all get the urge for a taster of things to come.

Brushing (2). Old comb being removed
for replacement by new foundation.

2. *Chemical repellents*. Certain substances with a strong odour are
disliked by bees who will retreat from them. The two most widely
used are proprionic anhydride and benzaldehyde. Both are
extremely volatile. Carbolic was used in the past but has fallen
from favour because its pungency tends to cling to the combs.

The method of application of the first two is to make a fume
chamber to the same dimensions as your hive and a few inches
deep — precise dimensions are not important. The lid of this
chamber is lined with absorbent material. Mix one measure of the
chemical with four measures of water and sprinkle the mixture over
the absorbent pad. Smoke the bees gently to start them moving

down, and place the fume chamber on top of the super in place of the cover board. Treat the next hive in similar fashion. Having done this, the super first treated will, with luck, be clear of bees. Remove this super immediately and cover. Repeat on next super down and so on.

This method only seems to work satisfactorily in warm, preferably humid, weather. Bees will not leave the super if there are any open cells and there is a slight danger that honey may be tainted if the chemical is used too strongly – this can also drive bees right out of the entrance in quantity. On the other hand, if it works the supers are cleared fairly rapidly and in one operation – no second visit to the apiary is necessary. This may well be a consideration if bees are kept some way away from home.

3. *Cleared boards.* These are usually made of three-ply timber framed to give a beeway on one side. They are exactly the same size as the hive body and bear two rectangular holes with rounded ends to take two 'porter' bee escapes. Most beekeepers make them do double duty by using them as inner covers when not in use as clearer boards, with the porter escape holes covered by perforated zinc or some such material. As bees hate draughts they will carefully close each hole in the zinc with propolis so you might as well save them work by using a piece of glass. This will be stuck down too but will give you a little peep hole to peer through at your bees, which you will feel impelled to do from time to time. It will do the bees no harm and give you some pleasure.

A porter escape is simply a one-way valve through which the bees can freely pass but not return. Two sets of light springs arranged in a V below the round entrance to the escape form the escape mechanism.

To use a clearer board, go to your bees one evening, gently lift off the super(s) to be cleared and remove the queen excluder, using a minimum of smoke, then place the clearer board on the brood chamber with the round hole of the escape uppermost. Replace the supers, together with their crown boards. In twenty-four hours, or perhaps forty-eight in cool weather, every bee will have gone down to join her sisters – with the exception of the five or six who never seem to know the rules. Ignore these. Quietly lift off the supers and take them away for extraction. This, I believe, is the method to be preferred. It can be done with a minimum of disturbance to the bees but it does involve two visits to the apiary. It is absolutely essential to see that all parts of the assembled hive are bee-tight. If there are any gaps, as fast as the bees go down they will come up on the outside, find the small gap and take your precious honey down into the brood chamber. It is just as likely that another colony will find the leak. The result is chaos and fighting. A bad case of robbing has to be seen to be believed and is difficult to stop.

Clearer board: one Porter escape has been fitted.

4. *Blowing.* Perhaps a brief mention might be made of a fourth method. A portable compressor or fan is used to create a powerful current of air and the bees are literally blown out of the supers. It is used by the 'big boys' in the United States and in Australia but is really only of passing interest to us.

Extracting

An extractor is simply a large centrifuge. It consists of a metal or plastic vessel, rather like a dustbin, in which is housed a cage that can be rotated, either by hand (usually) or by an electric motor (if you are very rich). Uncapped combs are placed in the cage, which is then revolved. Honey is extracted from the cells by centrifugal force, strikes the walls of the extractor and is collected in a space below the cage, from which it is drawn off via a tap.

Extractor: interior view to show handle, gearing and cage in which the uncapped frames of honeycomb are placed.

Two types of extractor are available. The first is the tangential type, where the combs are carried, as the name suggests, at right angles to the radius of turn, and the second is the radial type, where combs are loaded in racks radiating from the central spindle. The tangential (and usually cheaper) kind is more efficient since the force exerted on the open cells is greater than that on cells arranged radially. However, fewer combs can be loaded at one time so there is little difference in the energy expended in extraction.

When using a tangential extractor, remember that full combs of honey are heavy and also fragile. Rotate the cage at half speed for some fifty revolutions and then reverse the combs. Rotate steadily at maximum speed and then reverse again. In this way you will half empty the first side before putting full pressure on the second and so avoid undue strain and breakage. Radial extractors, of course, do not call for this reversing technique.

After extracting, the honey should be drawn off into some large container through a strainer to remove odd pieces of wax, and then allowed to settle for at least twenty-four hours – longer, if possible. This will let the bubbles rise and form a scum on the surface. The clear honey below can then be drawn off into 28 lb (12kg) tins for storage in a cool place until needed for bottling.

In all these extracting operations absolute cleanliness is essential. That old potting shed at the bottom of the garden will not do. Access to running hot and cold water is needed, so use the kitchen. You are bound to get honey on the door handles. Wipe this off as soon as you can, but if the family cut up rough about the stickiness, show them the beautiful tins of golden honey you have produced for the household!

Storing Food for Winter

Once the crop has been taken, September is the time for assessing the colony's food reserves and adding to them if necessary. It will need a minimum of 30 lb (14kg) of stores – more would be better. Any feeding needed should be completed by the end of the month. This will give the bees time to process the sugar syrup you give them and store it properly.

It is most unlikely that any district in the United Kingdom will have insufficient flora to provide pollen for your bees but it is necessary for them to have honey and/or processed sugar syrup to 'top up' the pollen cells and so prevent the contents from going mouldy during the damp, cold winter months.

Honey stores are another problem. It would be nice to say that the best winter stores for bees consist of natural honey. Unfortunately, research has shown that this is not necessarily the case. It all depends on your local flora. Some honies with a heavy protein or colloidal content are bad for wintering and the honeydew sometimes collected by bees is also unsatisfactory. During the winter months of long confinement to the hive, these stores lead to dysentry, disturbance, and maybe the death of many of the colony. Syrup made by dissolving 2 lb (900g) ordinary white granulated sugar in 1 pt. (575ml) hot water, then allowed to cool and given to the bees in a rapid feeder is much better. As far as it has been discovered, refined sugar has no deleterious effect on the adult bees of their offspring. Of course, if you have been a little greedy in taking 'your' surplus the need for supplementary feeding is that much more urgent.

How do you know how much stored food the bees have? There are indications that help. Have a quick look inside and assess how many frames have sealed food, and how full they are. A deep comb-full will hold perhaps 4 lb (1.8kg) of honey – 3 lb (1.3kg) is more likely if it is an old comb with a good deal of pollen.

Hook a domestic spring balance under the floor board at each side; lift enough to take the weight and add the two readings together. Make allowance for the weight of the hive and the empty frames. With a little experience, a good estimate can be had by 'hefting' the hive; that is, placing a hand under the floor board at the back and lifting gently. This is a bit hit-and-miss but it is certainly easy to detect whether a hive is light (needs food) or heavy (is adequately stocked). The grey area in the middle is the difficulty. When in doubt feed.

Preparing for Winter
October will often bring a week or so of good flying weather which will enable the bees to collect some late pollen (ivy and late michaelmas daisies), process their stores and arrange them in an arch-shaped segment at the top of the combs. As soon as this fine spell ends, mouse guards must be placed over the entrance. Do not delay – a few cold nights and the mice will be in.

From this point on do not disturb the joints between boxes and between the inner cover and the top box. Remove the feeder.

There are two schools of thought about ventilation. One is to cover

Checking the weight of the hive with a spring balance.

the feed hole with a piece of perforated zinc or glass and then add a dry sack or something similar on the inner cover below the roof. The other is to leave the feed hole uncovered so that there is through ventilation. This, it is claimed, avoids the possibility of mouldy combs during the winter. On balance, the ventilation idea is preferable. It is true that bees can and do stand a great deal of cold, dry weather providing they have ample food, but do badly in damp conditions. Make sure that the roof is weathertight and sits down evenly on the boxes.

When using a feeder or adding packing on top of the inner cover, space is needed. This is often provided by an empty super but I think a better, and cheaper, scheme is to make a simple box about 4 inches (10cm) deep to the exact dimensions of the *outside* of the hive (I am assuming that you are using a single-walled hive). The thickness of the material is of no importance as no frames are to be hung in it, nor do you need any rebates or shoulders. The idea is to provide space between the roof and the inner cover. I leave mine on all the year round and I fancy that the air space so created helps to keep the hive cool in very hot weather. Use whatever material you have to hand. Offcuts of chip board are quite satisfactory with short lengths of 1 inch (2.5cm) square timber in the inside corners for rigidity.

During November and December leave well alone apart from seeing that the roof is secure. Two bricks on the roof will hold it down if you get a spell of windy weather. In December, if you have doubts as to whether you fed adequately in the autumn, put a cake of candy over the feed hole. If the bees want it they will take it down; if not, they will ignore it. Here again, it may be said that this is an 'unnatural' way of feeding and that it is better not to use refined white sugar. Whatever the arguments, and they may be cogent, the choice may be between a live colony and one dead of starvation. Faced with this choice most of us would, I am sure, prefer the live colony. But it must be said that the use of candy is a rescue operation and is not for routine.

During the winter, read all you can. Attend association meetings and lectures. You will get much contradictory advice. Listen to it all and make your own decisions. Beekeeping is more an art than an exact science. This is a good time to make spare equipment for next year. Extra hives and everything that goes with them — inner covers/clearer boards, supers, nucleus hives, feeders and so on, are all best made in the winter months. If you wait until the summer months and you find that you need something urgently for expansion or the odd swarm, you will be caught out.

Breeding

Breeding will start in a small way in January. Towards the end of the month, feel the inner cover for warmth. A nice gentle feeling of warmth will tell you that egg laying and brood rearing is well in progress. For interest, give the side of the hive a sharp rap. A strong hiss rapidly dying away means all is well and the queen is doing her duty. A weak hiss means a small cluster. A prolonged roar after the hiss probably means queenlessness, food shortage or possibly disease. Food shortage can be remedied with a cake of candy but there is little that can be done at this time for more serious troubles other than to seek advice from more experienced beekeepers. Your diagnosis may be wrong.

In February, do not disturb but just see that all is well externally.

More colonies die from starvation in March and April than at any other time of the year. Egg laying and brood raising is now well advanced and demands for food increase daily. During the cold winter months the bees will hang in a tight cluster with their metabolic rate at a low level so that food consumption will be very low – it could be only a few ounces a week. In March, however, the bees' biological clock says that the time has come to start raising young whatever the outside weather conditions are. The temperature at the centre of the cluster must be raised to about blood heat and this can only be done by the consumption of stored honey and the production of heat by movement and the processes of digestion.

Food, both honey and pollen, is needed to stimulate development of the nurse bees' hypopharyngeal glands so that they may produce brood food. After the first few days of life the young brood will need to be fed with a honey/pollen mix. Ample supplies of pollen are essential and brood cannot be raised without it. These food demands are cumulative and the truth of the old beekeepers' saying that 'Spring feeding is best done in the autumn' now becomes clear.

It is difficult to make good any pollen shortage, but this is not likely to occur in most areas of the UK. Late summer and autumn flowers are usually so abundant in our much maligned climate that the bees will have packed away enough, except in very exceptional autumn weather conditions when flying is restricted. Still, it is reassuring to see the bees hurrying into the hive on a warm, sunny day with their bright yellow loads of crocus pollen – another sign that all is well.

If a quick heft at the back of the hive seems light and you are not happy about honey reserves, a feed of warm sugar syrup can now be given. Remember that if you start feeding you must continue to do so steadily until fruit blossom is out or there is an alternative natural supply of nectar available.

Spring Examination of the Hive

As soon as you get one of those early April warm days it is possible to lift off the inner cover and have a quick look down between the combs. Try to see how much sealed stores are visible and how the bees are spreading outwards. How many 'seams' of bees are there? Do not disturb the combs in any way. Be quick about this first look – but not jerky – and replace the inner cover as soon as your curiosity is

photograph courtesy of E.J. Piper.

Examining a brood comb.

satisfied. If you have a clean spare floorboard this can be used to replace the old one which will now be covered with a circular patch of debris.

The first week in May is early enough to think of a frame-by-frame examination, and then only if the weather is calm, warm and sunny. It is not necessary to see the queen. If you see eggs and very young larvae you will know that she is there. Brood can easily be chilled at this time of the year by keeping the hive open too long in a search for the queen. The opportunity can be taken to note any misshapen and old combs. These can be moved to the outsides in later manipulations for replacement with fresh frames of foundation. Continue to feed steadily if nectar is not coming in. Towards the end of May an old queen will often show signs of failing by a falling off of the quantity of eggs laid, and of course the quantity of brood.

And this is just about where we came in.

4

THE NATURAL HISTORY OF THE HONEYBEE

Two terms are often used to indicate a family of honeybees as a going concern — a 'stock' and 'colony'. Throughout this book the word 'colony' is used to denote the community of bees themselves, queen, drones and workers. By 'stock' we mean a colony housed within a hive.

The Queen
The queen is the only complete female within the colony. Her function is to lay eggs. She mates only once during her lifetime, although this is usually a multiple mating; that is, she mates with a number of drones, perhaps as many as seven or eight, on one or two successive days, after which no more mating takes place. Mating invariably takes place in the air and few beekeepers have ever had the chance to witness the act. It has recently been discovered that there are 'drone congregation areas' to which virgin queens on mating flights resort, if that is the word.

Once perceived by the drones she plays 'hard to get' and flies rapidly away, pursued by the drones, with the result that the strongest and swiftest drones catch up with her and couple. At the moment of copulation the genital organs of the drone evert from his body and semen is ejaculated into the queen's vaginal orifice, immediately followed by a plug of mucus which quickly hardens in the air. The drone falls and dies. It is believed that subsequent successful drones dislodge this plug when mating but the now mated queen eventually returns to the hive bearing the mating sign, the genital organs of the last drone she has coupled with.

On her return, the workers recognize the change in her. They follow her over the combs, clean her and offer her food. Within forty-eight hours or so she begins to lay eggs. The spermatozoa she receives on mating is stored in a special flask-shaped organ, the spermatheca, and is kept viable for the whole of her life which may be as long as five years unless the beekeeper chooses to bring in a new queen earlier. At her peak in early summer she is capable of laying 2000 or more eggs in twenty-four hours. Her abdomen is almost completely filled with two ovaries and her rate of laying is controlled by the amount of royal jelly fed to her by the workers. Developing eggs pass down ovarioles, slender tubes starting as fine threads high in the abdomen, just below the heart. The egg cells originate here and increase in size as they mature and grow until they are discharged into a median oviduct fully developed. As the eggs pass down the oviduct when the queen is in the act of laying they pass the opening of a small duct leading from the spermatheca. The queen can, at will, either let the egg pass through unfertilized, in which case it develops into a drone (the male bee), or she can release a small quantity of sperms which fertilize the egg. It can then develop into either another queen or a worker.

This choice is possible because of parthenogenesis — the ability of eggs to develop without having been fertilized, a process common among insects. The rather curious result is that the drones have a mother but no father, a fact which is utilized by research workers breeding a 'true line' by instrumental insemination. Different theories are held as to what prompts a queen to fertilize or not. Perhaps it is the size of the cells. Drone cells are about $\frac{1}{4}$ inch (6mm) in diameter, workers cells about 1/5 inch (5mm).

The Role of the Queen

Apart from egg laying, the queen plays an essential part in maintaining colony morale. She is constantly cleaned and licked by attendant workers, who, in doing this, acquire minute quantities of a substance exuded from glands near her mandibles. For want of a better word, and perhaps there is none, this is known as queen substance. As there is constant food exchange taking place, even more minute quantities of queen substance are distributed through the colony until every member has her share. Experiments have shown that sugar syrup containing a radio-active tracer fed to bees will make every individual in the colony radio-active within twenty-four hours.

The effects of queen substance are at least two-fold. In the first place, it seems to promote cohesion and keeps the workers content to go about their duties, and secondly it inhibits the building of queen cells, the cells in which new queen larvae are reared.

Most virgin queens reach full maturity about seven to ten days after emergence, but because of bad weather they may not be able to fly and mate for some time after this. After three weeks it becomes impossible for them to mate. They may then be fed by the workers but will only be able to lay drone (unfertilized) eggs. Unless helped by the beekeeper, such a colony will perish in a few months.

Workers

Workers are sexually undeveloped females. They arise from fertilized eggs which hatch in three days, but whereas queen larvae are fed entirely on royal jelly, after two-and-a-half to three days worker larvae are weaned on a mixture of honey and pollen. Growth is rapid and nine days after the egg is laid the cell is sealed with slightly porous cappings. The larva then spins a silken cocoon and pupates. A number of metamorphoses and moults take place and twenty-one days after the egg is laid the perfect adult insect emerges.

For many years it was thought that the bodily differences between the queen and the worker were entirely due to the coarser diet fed to the latter. It is hard to believe that this is the sole reason and it may be that there are differences between the brood food fed to worker and queen larvae. The appendages on the legs of workers, for example, are exactly fitted for the collection of pollen, the number of facets on the eyes differ, the worker's sting is straight and barbed, the queen's sting is curved and not barbed. These are a few of the many physical differences. The worker is much more than a stunted female. It may be that minute traces of glandular secretions are added to the food by nurse bees and that these differ between queens and workers. Recent research shows that cell growth is directed and controlled by very small differences in the molecular structure of body cells in all organisms.

After emerging and drying off, the young worker spends a few days gathering her strength and cleaning cells (the queen will not lay in a cell unless it has been cleaned and polished) and then begins to feed older larvae with the pollen/honey mixture. As special glands in her head develop, become active and exude the special brood food, the younger larvae are fed. During this time as house bees they also receive pollen and nectar from returning foragers and pack this into cells, even if only temporarily. Nectar contains a large proportion of water and much of this has to be evaporated.

Temperature and humidity within the hive have to be carefully controlled between limits and this is accomplished by groups of bees standing on the floor of the hive fecing outwards and fanning their wings rapidly. A similar group will be on the other side of the entrance, also fanning but facing inwards. In this way a current of warm moist air is drawn out of the hive on one side and cool dry air drawn in on the other. One of the most pleasant experiences oe any beekeeper is to visit his hives in the cool of the evening in the summer after a day of nectar flow. The delightful perfume of evaporating nectar meets him some distance from the hives and the steady hum of the fanners is an augury of things to come.

On sunny days, around midday, the young nurse bees will come out for short play fights beginning with close-in semi-circles but gradually widening further afield. These play flights serve two purposes. Bees will not tolerate any dirt in the hive and faeces are always voided in flight – unless the colony is seriously diseased. The rectum is capable of considerable distension allowing faeces to be retained during inclement weather when flight is not possible. There is evidence that a recycling process operates, removing surplus water from the rectum and returning it to the body cavity, thus relieving pressure and reducing the necessity for water foraging. In the second place, the play flights enable the young worker to recognize the surroundings and to fix orientation points in her memory for use in navigating home.

Foraging

When they are ten or twelve days old, the workers can become foragers for nectar, pollen and water according to colony needs, and from twelve to eighteen days they are physiologically able to produce wax from specialized glands on the ventral side of the abdomen. After eighteen days they become full-time foragers, scouring the surrounding countryside in search of nectar, pollen and propolis. These dates and times can be, and frequently are, varied to respond to shortages of stores or other needs of the colony. It is interesting to speculate what prompts the workers to do any particular job at a particular time. There is no overseer to direct their labours. Because of the constant exchange of food, differences of quantity and quality are quickly perceived by many of the colony members in a very short time and they react accordingly. The two most important factors in the life of a bee seem to me to be an inherited set of behaviour patterns and, arising from this, the ability to react to environmental conditions automatically.

Workers have rudimentary ovaries and in normal circumstances these remain atrophied but should an accident befall the queen so that there are no eggs or young larvae available, the ovaries of some of the workers may develop and they will lay eggs – often in a haphazard pattern and with several eggs in one cell. These eggs can only hatch and develop into stunted drones. The laying workers do not differ in outward appearance from their sisters and the situation which arises is difficult to cure. The colony with many laying workers will often refuse to accept a replacement queen. The condition is not too common.

What is said in the paragraphs above, and indeed in the whole of this book applies to the indigenous honeybee of Western Europe (*Mellifera mellifera*) wherever she has been transported. Other bees, other habits. For instance, a race of bees found in South Africa (*Mellifera capensis*) normally has numbers of laying workers and these are capable of laying eggs which develop into queens.

Drones

Drones are the male bees and they arise by parthenogenesis from unfertilized eggs. Most colonies will build patches of drone cells in the lower corners of their brood combs. Drones are only bred during the summer months and indeed their presence in a winter colony is an indication of queenlessness. In the active months the presence of a few drones seems to aid colony morale. The drone certainly gives the impression of being an amiable fellow in a bumbly, noisy way and, of course, has no sting. His sisters feed him as required, and with very good sense he emerges from the hive only during the afternoons of warm sunny days. It is likely that his bodily heat helps to keep the temperature up in the hive, and therefore indirectly helps incubate the brood. On reaching full sexual maturity he will repair to drone congestion areas with his contemporaries. It is not altogether clear how these areas are selected. They are often at the head of shallow valleys. Perhaps wind current and air pressures are factors.

As with many other natural reproductive processes, only a very small proportion of drones ever achieve the object for which they are designed – and those that do die in the act. As autumn approaches, the remaining drones are pushed out of the hive by the workers. Early bee books used to say 'ruthlessly' or 'remorselessly' pushed out but I do not think that these emotive terms apply. There is no affection nor any ruthlessness. The drones are no longer needed so out they go, just as the queen is carefully tended and fed while she is needed but as soon as she fails as an egg layer or as the source of queen substance, a new queen is bred and the failing one neglected.

Queen, drone and Worker.

Senses

Within the hive the bee moves about her self-allotted tasks in total darkness, guided by an acute sense of taste and smell. Like most animals she seems to be able to distinguish between 'up' and 'down'. She is very sensitive to vibration and has a well-developed sense of touch but has no organs analagous to ears. She moves in an alien world compared with our own and is exquisitely adapted for doing so. Beekeepers might do well to remember this when they suddenly lift the usually opaque lids from their hives, letting in a flood of light – and, incidentally, upsetting the delicate balance of the colony's air conditioning systems.

Bees are sensitive to electro-magnetic fields, which they use in navigation, so under cross-country power lines is *not* a good place to site a hive. This response to magnetic fields also explains, at least in part, why bees tend to be bad tempered at the approach of summer storms with their enormous electrical discharges.

Their powers of sight differ markedly from ours. They cannot see the colour red (red flowers appear black to the foraging bee), but they are able to see farther into the other end of the spectrum and are very much aware of ultra-violet light. Many flowers which appear white to us reflect ultra-violet light in varying degrees and bees can distinguish these differences. The compound eye responds to flickers at frequencies of up to fifty-four per second but because of its construction the bee's visual acuity is comparatively low. Each facet of the compound eye is separated from its neighbours by an opaque sheath with the result that the 'retina' of the bee's eye receives a number of dots of light of different intensity, making up a kind of mosaic vision. Flowers with strap-like petals moving gently in a breeze with colours in contrast to the background will therefore excite more interest than a large mass of unvaried colour and no broken pattern. A further aid to navigation is the fact that bees can appreciate the plane of polarization of light.

Of the various sugars to be found in nature, bees have, as might be expected, a marked preference for those common in floral nectar — sucrose, glucose and fructose — but can also distinguish between other more complex sugars to a greater extent than we are able. There are some curious differences. For instance, a carbohydrate rejoicing in the name of Octoacetyl sucrose is intensely bitter to man but apparently tasteless to the bee — a fact made use of in industry in 'denaturing' sugar so that it is quite useless for human consumption but acceptable to bees.

Bees are sensitive to floral perfumes in extreme dilutions and can 'smell' water at a distance. Their sense of smell is such that they can follow the scent gradient down the nectar guides on flower petals. Nectar guides are those lines on petals, often coloured, which lead down into the throat of the flower and towards the nectaries.

Communication
Communication between animals, and especially between animals

lacking the sense of hearing, is a vast study in itself and volumes have been written on the subject, but perhaps a very few words here would not be out of place. The famous 'bee dances' observed by Karl von Frisch spring to mind immediately as an example. They consist of rhythmic movements performed by a successful forager on her return to the hive in order, so it is said, to recruit more foragers to a fruitful source of food. The excited onlookers detect the particular perfume of the food source on the body of the dancer and by following her movements are directed to the food, both the direction and the distance according to the number of waggles per second in the dancer's waggle run. It is claimed that this latter information is not so much a question of mileage but of energy required. For instance, flight against a headwind would be indicated in a similar way to a longer mileage on a calm day. The following diagram is a simplified illustration of what happens.

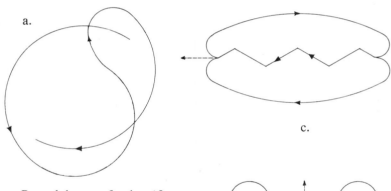

a. Round dance – food at 10m,
   no direction.
b. Sickle dance – food at 50-100m,
   in direction of arrow.
c. Waggle dance – food more than 100m.
   Slow waggle – distant food.
   Rapid waggle – food nearer.

In addition, the route becomes trail-marked by foragers who leave tiny traces of glandular secretions at strategic points to help guide newcomers. These substances are called pheromones. They are widely used in nature, especially in the insect world. Whereas hormones are substances released from glands within the body of the individual and induce responses within his body, pheromones are secretions emitted by one individual externally which elicit reactions on the part of another individual of the same species. The phenomenon has been known for a long time but recent research, which continues, suggests that the process is much more widespread than had been supposed and covers a wide range of behaviour patterns. For instance, there are pheromones which act as aphrodisiacs, provoke stinging, arouse alarm, and no doubt contribute to a host of other actions aiding survival of the individual and the species.

5

HANDLING BEES

Half the pleasure in keeping bees is to be had from the smooth and efficient handling of stocks with a minimum of disturbance, and leaving them after an examination working in much the same way as they were before you started. Half the people who give up beekeeping do so as the result of a disastrous experience with a thoroughly alerted and aggressive stock. The trick, of course, is not to let a colony get into this angry state. Work with your bees, not against them. If you find that a usually quiet stock 'boils up' when you open the hive this is quite likely due to some condition within the hive. Discretion is the better part of valour, so close up quickly and leave them alone for a few days. Try again and you will probably find that the mood has changed completely and they are their usual well-behaved selves.

I am sure that the best way of learning to handle bees — and it is not difficult to do so — is to take every opportunity of watching a real bee artist at work, and to assist if possible by acting as his 'smoker boy'. It will seem as if he has some kind of magic touch which enables him to handle the bees and to move frames about, even to scoop up handfuls of bees, with impunity and without causing any kind of uproar. It is not true, of course; neither is the widely held belief (by non-beekeepers) that bees know their owner. Watch carefully and you will see that everything he does he does gently. He moves slowly and deliberately and always has any equipment he will need close to hand. He clearly likes bees and is familiar with their habits so that he can interpret their moods and anticipate their reactions to conditions. I do not suggest that you will become such a person overnight — it has probably taken him a lifetime of beekeeping to reach this blissful state — but I do suggest that you can achieve some of this expertise with a little thought and practice (and, incidentally, be much admired for it by your non-beekeeping friends).

Beginners, remembering all they have been taught and all they have observed about handling bees, will often do so successfully in a short time. After a while they may become a little over-confident and bang a stock about or open up in unsuitable weather. They get a sharp reminder from the bees to be more careful in future. As in other walks of life, it pays not to take liberties!

If the following points are borne in mind, the road to success will be that much quicker.

A bee cannot withdraw her sting after thrusting it into the resilient flesh of a warm-blooded animal and so she will not use it except under provocation or in panic. Her hereditary enemies are marauding animals and birds, and forest fires. She has two very powerful instincts — to collect nectar whenever it is available and to protect the colony, especially when young brood is present. Most swarms can be handled with ease. This may be due to two factors. The bees will have gorged themselves on honey before issuing in search of a new home and there will be no brood present to defend. A colony will, in a very short time, behave according to the reactions of the individual bees composing it. Annoy a few bees and the colony will quickly become alerted and aggressive. Frighten 10 per cent into gorging honey and soon many more will follow suit.

Things Which Lead to Contentment
Presence of brood, a laying queen and plenty of stores with a few open cells.

Quiet deliberate movements.

Unobstructed flight path. (Do not stand in front of the hive.)

Warm, still weather.

A nectar flow.

Keeping the combs covered.

Clean, smooth, light-coloured covering cloths and clothing. A white cotton boiler suit is ideal. Some beekeepers say that nylon clothing annoys. I think that this may be so if movement and rubbing induce an electric charge on the nylon. Bees in flight, and on the combs, carry an electrical charge and a nearby large mass with a high potential might well reverse the polarity on the bees. 'Touchiness' in bees at the approach of a thunderstorm is well known.

Things Which Frighten

Smoke (perhaps due to an inherited fear of forest fire).
Rhythmic drumming on the outside of the hive.

Things Which Subdue and Control

Proper (not excessive) use of cool, aromatic smoke.
Fine spray of water.
Sprinkling with weak sugar solution.

Things Which Annoy

Sudden movements across the tops of exposed frames.
Jarring and the jerk when a stuck frame is prised loose.
High winds and cold weather.
Thundery weather.
Human breath.
Perspiration.
Hairy clothes, especially if brown.
Crushing bees.

With these points in mind, when you prepare to do your first solo manipulation choose a day when it is calm and warm. Mid-afternoon is best. If you can see that the bees are bringing in a little nectar, so much the better. Wear a clean white boiler suit or a light-coloured linen jacket past its best days, a veil, trouser legs tucked into wellingtons, and gloves. Make sure your smoker is well alight. Old sacking or rolls of corrugated paper will do. So will *dry* rotted wood or a piece of old propolized bee quilt, but you are unlikely to have acquired this in the early stages. Have spare smoke fuel and a box of matches in your pockets, and your hive tool, cover cloths and a spare brood chamber, if you have one, ready to hand. I like to have a well-washed washing up liquid container filled with weak sugar syrup (1 lb (450g) sugar to 1 pt. (575ml) water.

Make a Plan

Have a clear plan. There is no point in opening a hive unless you have in your mind a clear idea of what you propose to do or look for. Stand behind the hive and try to move your feet as little as possible. Smoke the entrance with three or four medium puffs. Wait two minutes. The smoke will frighten the bees and make them rush to open cells and gorge themselves with honey. Others will soon join in. The maximum effect of smoke occurs in two to three minutes. During this time you can be quietly taking off the roof and any packing materials on the inner cover. Gently lay the roof, upside down, on the ground to your left. No banging, please.

Remove the supers or inner cover by inserting your hive tool at a corner between the supers and the queen excluder or between the inner cover and the brood chamber, as the case may be. Lever upwards a little, smoking the crack gently. Make sure that no frames are stuck and are being lifted.

Once you start lifting, carry on slowly, or pause if you have to, but do not lower. If you have to change your grip, keep the boxes apart with the hive tool. Bees will be running about on the frame tops in the gap you will have created and the last thing you want to do is to crush any of them. If there are no supers, look very carefully at the underneath of the inner cover as you remove it. The queen could be there. If she is, put her gently back into the hive.

Remove the queen excluder in the same way, again looking carefully for the queen on the underside. Cover the frames with one of your cover cloths. This should be big enough to hang down a few inches on either side. Roll back the cover cloth until one frame is exposed. Free this carefully with your hive tool, lift by the lugs and hang it in the spare brood box. If you do not have a spare box, the frame can be stood on the ground at the side of the hive and towards the entrance. Again, examine it carefully for the queen. It is unlikely that she will be on an outside frame. These are generally used for stores – unless the queen is getting short of laying space!

Inspecting the Frames

You are now in a position to go through the whole colony frame by frame and in comfort. The frame you have removed will give you working space. Roll back the cover to expose the next frame and put your second (rolled) cover cloth at the edge of the brood box so that by rolling up one and unrolling the other you never have more than one frame exposed at a time. This will keep the brood nest fairly dark and prevent the bees boiling up between the frames. All your movements should be slow and deliberate. Do not pass your hands over the top of the brood chamber even when it is covered with a

Summer examination (British National Hive with two shallow supers).

cloth. Try to get into the habit of moving your hands round the outside of the box to the frame you want to lift, and then do so by the lugs.

Bees *will* propolize frames to runners and to neighbouring frames — especially if your carpentry has not been too accurate. Use your hive tool to prise them free — but gently — that wrenching jerk is just the thing to arouse the bees. Never turn a comb so that it is horizontal. Always keep it vertical and hold the frame you are examining over the hive. If the queen should drop off she zill land in the hive or on your cover cloth — not in the long grass round the hive you have been meaning to clip but never seemed to get round to it. By lowering one hand and raising the other and then turning the frame by the lugs, both sides can be scanned. Use smoke sparingly and always puff it across the frame tops, never down between the frames. Carry out your examination smoothly and without haste but also without undue delay. It is not always necessary to take out every frame — indeed, I would go so far as to say that it is seldom necessary except when looking for queen cells or similar operations. For instance, if your object is to make sure that the colony is queenright (a colony is said to be queenright when it is headed by a mated and fertile queen), you do not need to see the queen. As soon as you find eggs or young larvae, you know and can close up at once. In the unlikely event of there being no cells in sight which are open and contain honey, score a few in the honey arch with your hive tool so that the bees have an unobstructed access to the honey.

Any odd bits of wax or brace comb you scrape off the top bars should be put in an old tin. To leave these pieces lying around will only encourage robbing.

6

SWARMING AND INCREASING

All living organisms must reproduce their kind if the species is to survive. This is so essential that natural selection has ensured that the urge to reproduce is a very powerful one indeed.

In the case of the bee, reproduction has a twofold aspect. In the brood nest at the height of the season hundreds of young bees emerge every day to replace their older sisters whose summer occupations have literally worked them to death. I sometimes think that a bee is rather like a wound-up clock. Both start life with a fixed amount of stored energy and when this is gone the machinery stops. This, of course, is an over-simplification, but the analogy does help to explain, partly at least, why the life of an individual worker bee from egg to death may be no more than six to seven weeks in the summer while bees hatched from eggs laid in the autumn survive well into the spring – a matter of six months. This is individual reproduction in order to keep the colony at strength. However, because bees are social creatures and can only exist in colonies, the colony is the unit of survival and must reproduce itself if the species is to survive.

A honeybee colony is potentially immortal. The individuals are replaced but the colony is inherently capable of continuing for a very long time indeed. Think of a river at any precise point. The water flowing past this point is constantly changing but the river remains. No colony can die of old age. Of course very few, if any, colonies achieve this potential immortality. Many die from disease, the actions of predators and other enemies, starvation or some accident of nature. Over the ages, bees have evolved a mechanism of colony reproduction which incorporates a built-in system of restraint. If it were not for some degree of restraint there would be the likelihood of colonies dividing again and again, giving rise to enormous numbers of small daughter colonies too weak to sustain themselves during the cold winter months.

The queen honeybee, unlike the queen wasp and the queen bumble bee, cannot fend for herself in the early stages of colony development and needs attendant workers to feed and care for her. Therefore there must be an arrangement for the rearing of one or more queens within the colony which, at the appropriate time, splits into separate entities. In its simplest form each has its own queen with enough workers of all ages and some drones to form viable units. One group remains in the old hive and the others take off to find a new nesting site. This method of colony division is what we call swarming.

Some Reasons for Swarming

In the section on natural history I have referred briefly to the way attendant workers are constantly licking and grooming the queen and so getting minute quantities of queen substance which is then rapidly spread throughout the colony via food sharing. One effect of these infinitely small quantities of queen substance is to stop workers from building queen cells. It seems odd that for most of the time colony harmony depends on the workers being prevented from obeying a natural instinct, but it is so. The natural instinct of workers is to build queen cells all the time, but queen substance, a pheromone, holds this instinct in check. The consequence of this arrangement is that if the workers fail to get their regular ration of queen substance their inborn instinct comes into play and they immediately start to build queen cells — an automatic response which will operate if the queen fails for any reason, such as age, disease, accident, or perhaps over-population.

Colonies headed by young and vigorous queens in their second season are less likely to swarm than those with old queens whose supply of queen substance may be tailing off. The queen substance theory is only a part, and a small part, of the story of swarming; theories as to its why's and wherefore's are almost as numerous as beekeepers.

Some strains of bees are inveterate swarmers and are best got rid of. Others are less likely to do this and frequently 'supersede'. That is, a new queen is raised, she mates, returns to the hive and lives for a short time alongside the old queen quite amicably. When the young queen is in full lay, food offered to the old queen is gradually withheld and she finally dies and is removed. This supersedure is really a kind of internal swarming and occurs more frequently than is sometimes thought. The old queen in a swarm is usually replaced in this way as soon as the swarm has settled down in its new nesting site.

Many beekeepers make a habit of marking their queens with a small dab of quick-drying paint on the thorax. This seems to do them no harm and certainly is a great help in finding them during the populous summer months. If the practice of marking young queens is carried out it is immediately apparent that supersedure has taken place if a young unmarked queen is discovered in the hive and there is no sign of the old marked queen.

It is also a fact that many colonies make preparations for swarming during the summer, which later become abortive. Circumstances both within the hive and outside may change quite rapidly causing the bees to 'change their minds' and abandon swarming preparations. Practically all colonies construct queen cups – the bases of queen cells – along the lower edges of brood combs. Most of them are never

photograph courtesy of E.J. Piper.

Typical swarm.

drawn out into full queen cells but are always there for use. Of the many theories put forward to explain just why a colony decides to swarm at a particular time the favourites are: an excess of young nurse bees with not enough larvae to feed; an excess of bees of wax-making age with congestion and no space for comb building.

The truth is that so far no really fully satisfactory explanation has been put forward and there is no system of swarm control which will guarantee complete absence from swarming but there are one or two points to be borne in mind which will reduce its incidence. Have your colonies headed by young queens of a known record of low swarming and avoid congestion when the colony is developing rapidly by adding supers in good time and replace old misshapen combs with fresh frames of foundation.

Swarm Control

In spite of all your best endeavours sooner or later you will find your bees making preparations for swarming. During a routine inspection you will find queen cells in all stages and you should be prepared with a plan of action. The following is a simple method of swarm control which I have tried and found successful.

1. Add the first super early in the year when, say, six brood combs are covered with bees.
2. From May to July examine colonies at seven-day intervals, looking carefully for the beginnings of queen cells.
3. If you see unsealed queen cells, find the queen and place her, on the comb on which she is found, in a nucleus box or spare hive. This will be much easier to do if she has been marked.
4. Add a second comb of bees and sealed brood and a third comb with stores and some empty space for the queen to lay in.
5. Shake in bees from another comb and close the frames together to normal spacing. If you are using a full-sized hive body, close off the space left with a division board so that your three frames are confined between one side wall and the division board.
6. Provide a small entrance and move the nucleus you have made at least 10 feet (3.3 m) away.
7. Do not feed for three days but after this a little feeding will help to get the queen back into lay.
8. Go back to the parent hive. Examine each frame carefully and

destroy all large queen cells nearing completion and those with large larvae. Leave all other queen cells.

9. Push the frames together to normal spacing, being very careful not to damage any queen cells left. Add frames of drawn comb if you have any. If you have none, close up with a division board, as in the case of the nucleus.

10. Eight days later carefully examine all frames again and select one good-sized queen cell, preferably on the face of a comb. Destroy all others. Make *quite* sure that you have not overlooked any. Shake the bees off combs if necessary so that you can get a good look, but do not shake the comb with the selected queen cell.

11. Re-assemble the hive. The virgin queen will emerge, mate and head your colony and it is most unlikely that the colony will make any more preparations for swarming that year so it will not be essential to examine for queen cells any more until the next season.

Re-uniting the Colony

What you have done is to re-queen your colony with a young queen of your own strain and, at the same time, have made a nucleus which can be built up into a full-sized colony if you want to increase the number of your colonies. If you do not desire to increase, the nucleus can be united with the parent colony later after the new queen has settled down (during a nectar flow is a good time). Find the old queen in the nucleus and destroy her. Go to the parent colony and place a sloping board from the ground to the entrance. Remove the division board if this is still in. Shake the bees from two or three combs on to the board, being careful to see that you are not shaking the queen down with them. Immediately shake the bees from the nucleus on top of the bees on the board. The parent hive can be completed with the combs from the nucleus. Re-assemble. Before this operation, gradually move the nucleus 2 feet (60cm) at a time until it is close to the parent hive.

There is a second, and very easy, method of uniting which can be used, not only after a re-queening operation, but on any occasion when it is found necessary to unite two colonies. One evening when flying has ceased, remove the roof from the parent colony and also any covering you may have over the feed hole. Replace this covering with a sheet of newspaper and make two or three pin holes in it. Cover this with a queen excluder. Place an empty brood box over it and transfer the combs from the nucleus to it, having removed the queen first. If you cannot find her, look the next day. The queen excluder will prevent her going down into the present colony but it is much better to search for her first, and destroy her. The bees will amalgamate through the newspaper and the nucleus combs can be removed in a couple of days.

Increasing Your Colonies

1. *By nuclei.* The first method is to take a nucleus formed with an old queen as described above under the swarm control method, and simply built it up. At this stage you may like to consider re-queening with a mated queen bought from a reputable queen breeder or from a friend with a good strain of bees. If you do so decide there are one or two considerations to be borne in mind, for a colony, even if queenless, may not accept a strange queen without some preparations being made.

The colony must be queenless so, once again, you will have to find the old queen and destroy her. It is a great help if the colony is now allowed to feed and groom a new queen without having full access to her and she must be induced to become acceptable to her new colony. This is not quite as difficult as it sounds.

Let us assume that you have bought a queen and that she has come to you through the post. She will arrive in a travelling queen cage with attendant workers and a little plug of candy to sustain them while on the journey. Place this cage on its side close to the open feed hole of your colony without removing the closures at the ends of the cage. Leave it for at least twenty-four hours.

Then take the cage indoors and open it by a closed window. The bees will fly to the light and the queen can be picked off. She is a very delicate creature and must never be squeezed. The trick is to pick her up by the wings. If you need to hold her – for marking, say – hold her by the legs with the thumb and forefinger of the other hand and then release the wings.

Place her in a cage made of $\frac{1}{8}$-inch (3mm) wire mesh. One end should be blocked with a plug of wood and one end left open. After the queen has been gently inserted, the open end should be closed with a small piece of newspaper secured by a rubber band. Such cages can be bought from any appliance manufacturer (they are known as 'Butler' cages) but can easily be made at home from a piece of $\frac{1}{8}$-inch (3mm) mesh wire gauge. No attendant workers should be in the cage with her. These can be collected in a matchbox and sent to one of the addresses given under 'Pests and Diseases' for examination as to health.

The cage containing the queen is then placed in the hive between two brood combs. The bees will feed and lick her through the wire gauze, hence the importance of the size of the mesh. The mesh on the travelling cage is too fine to permit this. The bees will eventually release her by chewing through the newspaper. Leave the colony undisturbed for at least seven days.

A nucleus can also be made by taking combs with an advanced queen cell from a colony preparing to swarm. Such a nucleus will need to be of reasonable size because it will have to remain in good heart until a young queen has hatched, mated and started laying. Two combs of emerging brood and two of food, plus the bees taken by shaking from two more combs is not too much. The nucleus will lose all the older flying bees who will return to the parent colony leaving only young nurse bees and those hatching out. The larger the nucleus the greater the chance of its survival and successful building up. By the same token the larger the nucleus the greater the damage to the parent colony. Only in exceptionally good years is it possible to break a colony to provide nuclei and get a honey crop at the same time.

2. *By making an artificial swarm.* There are a number of variations on this theme. Perhaps the most satisfactory way is to divide the colony so that a queenright portion without brood is left on the original site and all the brood is removed to another position. To do this, find the queen, place the frame with her on it in an empty brood box on the original stand and fill up with frames of foundation. A few frames of drawn comb, if you have any, are a help. Replace the queen excluder and the supers. Close up the frames in the original brood box adding one frame of foundation to replace the one you have taken away. Remove this box to a fresh site at least 15 feet (37cm) away (more if you can arrange it) on a new floor and with a new roof. All the flying bees will return to the old hive which will then have a powerful foraging force with no brood to feed. The queen will have

ample room in which to lay and it is unlikely that the colony will make
any swarming attempts that year.

The 'new' colony will raise a queen cell. If swarming preparations
have already been started, destroy all queen cells except one good
unsealed one. Alternatively, a young mated queen can be introduced
as already described. This new colony has lost its foraging force and
its food reserves in the supers so watch the food situation and feed if
necessary. Keep a small entrance to reduce the risk of robbing.

old hive

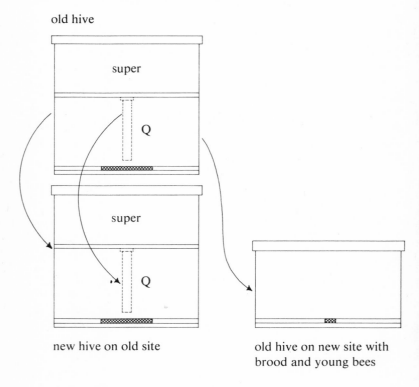

new hive on old site   old hive on new site with
                                brood and young bees

Making an artificial swarm: simple method.

7

PRODUCTS OF THE HIVE, WITH SOME RECIPES

The main object of beekeeping is the production of honey but, as we shall see, there are other substances to be found within the hive which, although of lesser importance, are nonetheless of value.

Honey
Honey is talked about a great deal but is rarely defined. In fact it is a delicately balanced, complex organic substance arising from natural sources and varying in small but significant degrees from flora to flora, county to county, and soil to soil.

The following is an average analysis:

	%
Water	17.2
Laevulose (fructose)	38.2
Dextrose (glucose)	31.3
Sucrose	1.3
Higher sugars	1.5
Maltose (reducing disaccharides)	7.3
Free acids	0.43
Lactone	0.14
Other acids	0.57
Minerals	0.169
Nitrogen	0.041

Plus enzymes (Diastase and invertase), vitamins, trace elements, inhibines, etc.

As an indication of the complexity, 'minerals' above includes minute but detectable traces of potassium, sodium, calcium, magnesium, iron, copper, manganese, phosphorus, sulpur, and 'trace elements' which include at least seventeen other elements.

This would be a good sample of honey with a fairly low water content. If this rises to much above 20 per cent wild yeasts can multiply, fermentation sets in and the honey will not keep well without pasteurization.

Crystallized Honey

Laevulose predominates in most honeys but in the case of rape and dandelion the proportion of dextrose is higher. Both these are simple sugars (monosaccharides) which can be assimilated into the human system without digestive effort. Their chemical composition is exactly the same but their molecules are arranged differently, resulting in a different crystalline structure, so that honeys with a high dextrose content crystallize out quickly. Indeed, rape honey will crystallize in the comb almost as soon as the bees have finished processing it — much to the consternation of the beekeeper who finds a box-full of combs solid with crystallized honey. The moral is, if you know that your bees are working rape do not delay, but extract as soon as the combs are 80 per cent capped.

If you have delayed and find solid honey, the only thing to do if you want it in jars is to scrape down to the midrib and heat gently — not more than 120°F (49°C). The liquid honey can then be run off at the bottom of the container — or the wax ladled off the top. A messy business altogether. After extraction, even if you have been in time, do not leave the honey in the settling tank for too long. There have been plenty of times when, after twenty-four hours in the settling tank, the whole lot has solidified. To find 50-100 lb (or 25-50kg) of honey in one lump is a little daunting.

In a sense, the trace elements, voltaile aromatic oils from the flowers and the enzymes added by the bees are more important than the sugar content. It is these which give honey its characteristic flavour and aroma and its health-giving properties. Excessive heating will drive off the volatile oils and destroy the enzymes which is why I have stressed the importance of only heating gently and only heating at all when it is really necessary. Of course, from the sales point of view, honey which has been pasteurized and pressure filtered will have a nice bright appearance, will look attractive and have a longer shelf life than your natural honey which can sometimes crystallize unevenly. The treated honey will have had its enzyme activity lowered, the aromatic oils driven off, at least partially, and have had most, if not all, of the included pollen filtered out. Can this really be described as 'honey'?

I believe that this delicately balanced natural food is worth preserving as nearly as is humanly possible in the same bio-chemical condition as it was in the comb, and my advice is do not mess it about more than you need to. Some people get over the problem by eating their honey in the comb and certainly there is a delicacy about the flavour of comb honey which is hard to describe but which is characteristic and unmistakable. If you want comb honey, use unwired thin foundation in your supers and remove combs as soon as they are capped, for cutting into suitable sized pieces. Heather honey, because of its 'non-drip' composition, is particularly suitable for this treatment. Heather honey has a thixotropic consistency and cannot be extracted in the usual way but has to be pressed out of the combs.

Comb Honey

If the honey is extracted, the combs can be returned to the bees for re-filling year after year. The bees will repair any damage you may do in uncapping. With comb honey, of course, the wax is lost. Bees have to consume a minimum of 10 lb (4.5kg) of honey from their stores to make 1 lb (450g) of wax so that in eating the comb honey you are appreciably diminishing your possible honey harvest. The other side of the picture is that bees need to have a certain amount of comb building when they reach a certain stage in development. As in most things a little moderation and common sense will pay dividends.

There are two kinds of honeydew. Both are collected by bees and in certain summers you may find your bees will have collected this, sometimes in considerable amounts. It tends to be dark in colour with a strong but not unpleasant flavour. It has a higher proportion of complex sugars than is the case in honeys of floral origin.

In Europe it is much preferred to floral honey and commands a considerably higher price. This is the well-known German Forest honey (Wald honig).

One kind of honeydew is the result of the action of aphids which suck plant sap and exude, through a kind of by-pass syphon, the sticky liquid they do not need. Common sources are beech, poplar, elm, oak, willow, lime, and conifers. The second is collected by bees from extra-floral nectaries which are quite common in such plants as beans, cherry, and laurels at the bases of the leaf axils.

Sources of English Floral Honey

The main sources of English floral honey are: clover; lime; heather (ling); fruit; sainfoin; mustard and charlock; hawthorn; sycamore; blackberry; willowherb; field beans; rape (increasingly). Apart from rape and ling, it is unusual to get a completely single floral source honey in the United Kingdom. For instance, a so-called 'clover' honey is likely to contain, say 70 per cent from clover with the balance made up from other local flora. Perhaps it is this admixture which makes the flavour of home-produced honey so much more attractive to most people than the uni-floral honies which are imported. On the other hand, some of these are good and I have tasted some pretty peculiar home-produced honies, so perhaps it is prejudice after all, but I really do think that, for the reasons outlined above, good home honey, cleanly handled with a minimum of filtering, has the edge over the imported item.

Beeswax

Beeswax is the second most important substance to come out of the hive. It has been used for thousands of years for embalming, candle making, writing tablets, modelling, casting metals in the 'lost wax' process. Nowadays it is used in industry and the cosmetic trade.

Wax cappings from honey comb are in demand by sufferers from asthma, respiratory troubles and hay fever – especially the latter. The theory is that by eating quantities of locally produced cappings the contained pollen sets up antibodies in the sufferer's system which mitigate allergic attacks. The treatment is best started months in advance of the period when attacks might be expected.

The melting point of wax lies somewhere between 143° and 147°F (62° and 63°C) according to the resins and other substances included.

Young bees secrete wax involuntarily at one stage of their development, or at least have a great urge to do so and it is good beekeeping to give these waxmakers something to do. An annual replacement of old or misshapen combs by frames of foundation will do just this and at the same time it aids apiary hygiene. Old comb is a happy hunting ground for disease organisms.

Wax has remarkable heat insulating properties. Some authorities have put it as high as 200 times that of resins and rubber. When extensive comb building is required – for instance, by a newly housed swarm – young bees hang in clusters holding each other by the legs, eat quantities of honey and exude wax scales from special glands on the ventral side of their abdomens. At 97°-98°F (36°C) these scales are pliable and can be worked and moulded in the bees' mandibles. Wax is expensive and not a scrap should be wasted. Save every piece, especially cappings, which produce the best wax, for rendering down.

There are a number of methods of doing this with heat and 'wax extractors' of wierd and wonderful design are on sale. Perhaps the easiest and cheapest way is to utilize the natural heat of the sun by making a solar wax extractor. Use any timber to hand to make a box not less than 18 inches (45cm) square; 2 feet by 2 feet (60cm by 60cm) is better. If it is smaller not enough heat is trapped. The box should be, say, 9 inches (22cm) deep. Add two legs to what will be the rear of the box so that it is propped up at about 30 degrees to the horizontal. Line the box with expanded polystyrene. Make a well-fitting lid consisting of a wooden frame double glazed. Horticultural glass will do quite well and the sheets should be about $\frac{1}{4}$ inch (6mm) apart.

Inside the box, arrange a large shallow metal tray (such as a meat dish) with a slot cut in the lower edge, the slot being covered with perforated zinc to retain odd bits of foreign bodies, cocoons, bees' legs, and so on. Raise this tray a little from the floor of the box to allow you to add a smaller receptacle to catch the molten wax which will seep through the perforated zinc gate. The amount of heat generated is quite astonishing – temperatures over that of boiling water have been recorded on a sunny summer day.

Old comb readily yields up its wax. I find it is best to cut the old comb into pieces and to stand the pieces in the metal tray with the cells sloping downwards. In this way the molten wax drains off and is not trapped in the cocoon-lined cells as will happen if the old comb is laid down as it is in the tray. Your rendered wax can be strained through surgical lint (*not* the boracic kind) and then cast into conveniently sized pieces – say 1 oz. (25kg) each. It can then be made into foundation, traded in for professionally made foundation or made into candles. Perhaps you will be able to spare an ounce or two to make some cold cream (see Recipes). This is absolutely first rate for rough or chapped hands in the winter.

Propolis, Royal Jelly and Pollen

There is always a demand for three other hive products — propolis, royal jelly and pollen.

Propolis is the resinous substance bees collect from plants and trees to stop up small cracks in their hives and to cement the various parts together — just to annoy beekeepers. It is a hard, gummy material, and the colour varies from light red to dark brown. It is soluble in alcohol and is the substance used by the famous Amati violin makers for the varnish for their instruments. It *can* give rise to a form of dermatitis in certain allergic people. In recent years there has been a demand for propolis following research conducted in Eastern Europe into its antibiotic properties which has resulted in its use as a cure for a large number of disorders, notably of the throat. In the UK it is sold in various forms in health food shops.

Royal jelly is also considered to be a nutritious food supplement. Perhaps it is, but the method of getting it is a deterrent to beekeepers. Basically, it means keeping colonies in a state of queenlessness as long as you can and collecting the royal jelly from the queen cells constantly being built. I personally do not find this a very attractive proposition.

Pollen also has its attractions for some as a diet supplement. To collect it, a grid is placed over the hive entrance so that the bees have to push through it to get in. In doing so the pollen pellets are dislodged from their legs and fall into a trough.

SOME RECIPES AND HINTS
Sugar Syrup

It used to be said that weak syrup (1 lb (450g) sugar to 1 pt. (575ml) water) should be fed to bees in the spring to 'stimulate' them and that in the autumn they should be given syrup made from 2 lb (900g) sugar to 1 pt. (575ml) water. I do not think there is a case to be made for the weaker sugar. If bees need feeding at all they need the syrup in the stronger concentration. Always use refined white granulated sugar, always give the feed in the evenings to avoid excitement and robbing, and never feed in excess of the bees' needs.

There has always been some discussion as to the desirability of feeding sugar at all but the facts are that in many parts of the United Kingdom weather may be bad at a crucial time of the year. There is a 'June gap' when spring flowers are over and the summer flora has not yet blossomed. This is at a time when bees are breeding heavily and their demands for food are considerable. In these conditions and in some years failure to feed will result in the death of the colony by starvation. This cannot be defended.

If the case of autumn feeding too, our climate is such that even a modest 'take' of honey will leave a colony with insufficient food to last the winter and supplementary feeding will have to be resorted to. I have known too many years when there has been no honey surplus at all and it has still been necessary to feed in the autumn. Feeding should not be carried beyond the point of necessity. Remember that the syrup you are feeding will be turned into bees. By not over-feeding you will avoid the possibility of any sugar syrup being carried into honey supers. Of course you should never feed when you have supers on your hives.

Making the syrup is simplicity itself; there is no need for any boiling. Simply dissolve the sugar in water; it will do so more readily in hot water than in cold. The recommended strength is 2 lb (900g) sugar to 1 pt. (575ml) water, as we have seen, but since metrication sugar now comes in 1kg bags. The extra 200g or so is of no importance so the drill is: a 1kg bag to 1 pt. (575ml) of very hot water. Let the syrup cool to a comfortable warmth before giving it to the bees.

If you are making syrup in fairly large quantities, a useful guide is to put the sugar into your chosen container, note the height it reaches and then fill with hot water to the same mark. Stir vigorously. This is only a rough and ready guide but the bees will process what you give them into the strength they need.

Candy

Candy is no more than confectioner's fondant, but uncoloured of course, and can be made at home for a fraction of the cost of the professional article. It is useful as extra food for the bees, as mentioned earlier in the book.

You need a large preserving pan, a cooking thermometer and a wooden spoon or spatula. The thermometer should read to 250°F (120°C) at least — most read to far higher temperatures than this. If you have to buy one specially, its cost will be repaid in the first batch of candy you make. You will then be able to further your popularity in the family by making coconut ice and all sorts of other goodies at just the right consistency.

Put 3 1kg bags of white granulated sugar in the preserving pan with 1 pt. (575ml) water. Stir until thoroughly mixed together. Place over heat and bring to the boil. Stir all the time.

Once the mixture boils there will be no danger of burning, so you can stop stirring. Turn down the heat until the syrup is boiling gently.

Place the thermometer in the boiling mixture and continue boiling until the thermometer reading is 235°F (113°C). The temperature at which the mixture boils is determined by the amount of water in it. At 235°F (113°C) the water content is just about what we need for a soft candy.

As soon as this temperature is reached turn off the heat. Allow to cool to 140°F (60°C) without disturbance. Then straightaway start to stir briskly with your wooden spoon or spatula. Soon the mixture will turn milky in appearance — in streaks first, then all over.

As soon as you reach this stage, pour the mixture into moulds to set — and be quick about it if you do not want to be left with an unmanageable set mass in your pan. Moulds can be anything you have of a convenient size. Aluminium cases for freezer foods and empty plastic ice cream containers are suitable, for example.

When cold, put the cakes of candy in a plastic bag sealed with a wire/paper tie until wanted.

Ideally, your candy should be soft enough when cold for you to press a thumb nail in but not so soft that it will 'move' and flow down between the combs when in use. The beauty of this method is that if you do happen to make a mistake and your candy comes out unsuccessfully — too soft or to hard — you can add water and start all over again. The only important factors are the two temperatures. You can also make syrup out of the unsuccessful candy — or any correct candy for that matter if need be.

Beeswax Candles
Try making a few candles the way our great-grandmothers did. This is

the dipping method.

Wax must never be melted in a vessel in direct contact with the source of heat – always use a water bath. The vessel chosen should be about 2 inches (5cm) deeper than the length of the candles you propose to make. Use the plaited cotton wick sold for the purpose in craft shops. First, melt the wax in a double vessel. Dip a length of cotton wick 3 inches (7.5cm) longer than your proposed candle into the wax. Remove it and straighten by allowing the wick to hang down and pulling gently on the lower end.

Start to dip with a regular motion – straight in and out. After each 'out' wait for 30 seconds to allow the coating of wax to solidify. Carry on dipping until the candle is as thick as you want. A knob of accumulated wax will collect at the bottom of the candle. Cut this off from time to time otherwise it will prevent your dipping down fully.

If your wax pot is wide enough there is no reason why you should not dip several candles at the same time. Tie wicks to a piece of wood, hold this horizontally and dip as described, taking care not to let the outside candles touch the sides of the wax pot.

Dipped candles take a very elegant tapered shape which is wider at the bottom than at the top.

Propolis Medication

Put 2/5 oz. (10g) of finely shredded propolis in a bottle with 1 3/5 oz. (40g) of rectified (96%) alcohol. Keep in a warm dark place for two days, shaking the bottle from time to time. Add water to make 4 oz. (100g) in all. Filter.

To use, add 1/5 oz. (5g) of the filtrate to half a glass of warm water and gargle. This is said to be effective against sore throats and ulcerated mouths.

Cold Cream

Melt 1 oz. (25g) light coloured beeswax and 1 oz. (25g) white vaseline in 5 fl.oz. (150ml) of liquid medicinal paraffin in a double saucepan (water bath).

Separately dissolve 1.4 grams of borax (about $\frac{1}{2}$ an apostle spoonful) in 1 fl.oz. (25ml) of distilled water.

Stir the two mixtures together to form a thick emulsion. The secret is to have the temperature of each liquid exactly the same, and not too hot.

Allow to cool a little and add a drop of floral perfume. (Or you can use rose water instead of distilled water earlier.)

Pour into small jars while warm.

This is first class for rough and chapped hands in the winter and is good used as a barrier cream too.

Grandmother's Cure for Irritated Throats
Mix 2 teaspoonsful liquid honey with 2 teaspoonsful glycerine and 1 tablespoonful lemon juice. A teaspoonful of the mixture works wonders.

Furniture or Floor Polish
Melt 8 oz. (225g) beeswax in 1 pt. (575ml) pure turpentine (white spirit will not do) in a jar in a pan of warm water, taking great care as the mixture is highly flammable. Pour into jars.

Mead
Mead is one of the oldest alcoholic drinks made by man. The following recipe will give a sweet mead, but you can make it dry by reducing the honey to 3 lb (1.3kg) and keeping the other items the same.

You will need:

4 lb (1.8kg) good quality honey

1 gal. (4.5 litres) clean water

Yeast. Formula '67', 'Mead' or 'Tokay' give good results; perhaps Tokay gives the highest alcohol content. The yeast can be bought at chain chemists or any wine makers' suppliers. Instructions for making a yeast culture are always given on the pack.

Yeast nutrient. A good formula for one gallon is:

Ammonium sulphate	60 grains
Magnesium sulphate	8 grains
Potassium phosphate	30 grains

A chemist will make this up for you but it is probably cheaper — and certainly quicker — to buy a packet of yeast nutrient already made up.

Juice of two lemons or $\frac{1}{2}$ oz. (12g) citric acid

$\frac{1}{4}$ teaspoonful Marmite

1 tablespoonful strong tea

Pinch of Epsom salts

A 1-gal. (4.5 litres) glass jar

Heat the water to 150°F (65°C). Add the honey, yeast nutrient, lemon juice, Marmite, cold tea and Epsom salts. Allow to cool to comfortable hand temperature (about 70°F or 21°C). Pour into the jar and add the yeast culture.

Plug the neck of the jar with cotton wool or insert a cork with a fermentation lock (wine makers' suppliers again).

Rapid fermentation will start within twenty-four hours and should continue for about a week. Rack off (that is, syphon off with a plastic tube) into a clean jar, leaving any sediment undisturbed. Insert the fermentation lock into the new jar or plug with cotton wool. Forget about it for two years.

During fermentation a steady temperature of about 70°F (21°C) is best. After the initial fermentation store in an even temperature if possible. A very slow secondary fermentation then takes place over a long period. Beekeepers all have their own special formulae for mead but the above is a reasonable starter.

8

HEALTH, PESTS AND NUISANCES

Bees conduct their affairs in such a clean way and are so intolerant of any kind of dirt that beekeepers should be on the alert for any sign of trouble and be prepared to help before the trouble becomes a disaster. There are a number of conditions, not all due to disease, which can affect bees from time to time. A few are serious but even the most minor have a weakening effect on the colony and will reduce its honey gathering capacity.

The important thing is to be able to recognize early signs that something is amiss, and then to act quickly or seek the advice of more experienced beekeepers. Such people are always to be found in Beekeepers' Associations and my experience has been that, almost invariably, they are ready to help the newcomer with advice and practical help.

Reference can be made, too, to Ministry of Agriculture Field Officers via the local Ministry Office. There is also that useful band of people, the County Beekeeping Lecturers. Alas, repeated governmental cheese-paring has reduced their number seriously, for losses by retirement or death have not been made good in many instances.

In order to see if anything is not quite right, it is necessary for the beekeeper to make himself familiar with the normal physical appearance of brood in all stages and also the normal pattern behaviour of adult bees. This is not as difficult as it sounds. During each manipulation and every time you have a quick look at the activity at the hive entrance, get into the habit of examining critically everything you can see. When you open a hive this need not, and should not, involve prolonged exposure of brood combs. You will quickly come to recognize the plump, creamy white glistening larvae neatly coiled at the bases of their cells and the khaki coloured sealed brood with slightly domed cappings. Any departure from this norm should be suspect and a reason found for it. It may be nothing very serious but it is as well to find out. The following catalogue of horrors will never be met by the beginner in total, and many beekeepers may never come across any of them.

Chilled and Starved Brood

Unsealed larvae shrivel and may be any colour from grey to almost black. Sealed larvae may have moist, sunken cappings a little similar to American Brood Disease (see page 84) but the cell contents are never 'ropy' (again, see American Brood Disease). The condition will arise if disease or a sudden cold spell result either in a contraction of the cluster or in a shortage of adult bees so that they are unable to cover the brood. Serious loss of bees due to poisoning can have the same effect.

It can arise through opening a colony too early in the spring and exposing the combs to cold, drying winds, or of 'spreading' too early in the year – that is, inserting empty combs into the brood nest in order to encourage a rapid build up. The bees will clear up the combs themselves.

Drone Brood

This may occur in irregular patches perhaps with small and under-nourished looking drones. The cause is most likely to be a failing queen and the obvious remedy is to re-queen or to unite the now depleted colony with a queenright colony – but make quite sure that no disease is present and remove the failing queen before uniting. When in doubt, seek a second opinion.

Sac Brood

Sac brood is a virus disease which attacks the thorax and abdomen of brood in the pupal stage. Affected pupae form tough little bags (sacs) filled with fluid. Adult bees can be affected too; this is the only disease, I think, which can affect both brood and adult bees. There is no known cure but the symptoms often disappear with a good nectar flow. It is likely to flare up when a colony has been badly disturbed or otherwise subjected to stress conditions.

Chalk Brood

This is a fungal disease affecting larvae which become a mass of mycelium giving the characteristic 'chalky' appearance. Later, small black fruiting bodies appear on the mycelium and release hundreds of spores to keep the infection going. Dampness and bad ventilation provide the conditions in which the fungus thrives. There is no known cure.

Advice on the above minor brood troubles is given in Ministry of Agriculture Advisory leaflet 561 (see Appendix 3). They are troublesome but will usually yield to treatment. The two brood diseases which follow are much more serious.

American Brood Disease

Bacterial infection, the spores of which are extremely resistant to heat, cold and dessication, cause this disease. They can lie dormant for many years and re-activate in suitable conditions – the body of a bee larva, for instance. Only brood is affected. It is a notifiable disease and destroying the bees (after they have been killed) and all comb by fire is the only treatment.

The hive in which an infected colony has been found should on no account be used again until it has been thoroughly sterilized inside and out. This can be done by scrubbing with a strong solution of washing soda, but it is far better to 'flame' all surfaces with a blow lamp, paying particular attention to all corners and crevices.

The disease is subject to the provisions of the Foul Brood Diseases of Bees Order 1967. This is administered by Ministry Foul Brood Officers. Seek their help at your local Ministry Office if in doubt.

Larvae die after the cells have been sealed. Cell cappings become dark and greasy looking. The larvae collapse and form a gelatinous mass. If a matchstick is pushed into a cell with a diseased larva, then twisted and withdrawn, some of the cell contents will come out in a slimy thread attached to the matchstick. This 'ropiness' is very characteristic and is most unlikely to be found in any other condition.

The larvae gradually turn dark brown, or even black, and eventually form scales adhering very firmly to the lower angle of the cell. These are a mass of spores. It is in trying to clean up the cells and remove the scales that the house bees carry the infection to the larvae they feed, although they themselves are not affected.

European Brood Disease

This is also a bacterial disease. In this case the larvae die before the cells are sealed. Infected larvae seem to wander about restlessly in the cell instead of remaining in the normal coiled position, and die in unnatural twisted attitudes. The remains may be sticky and like soft porridge but are never 'ropy' as described under American Brood Disease.

Treatment is either destruction by fire, as in the case of American Brood Disease, or by dosing with an antibiotic (terramycin) at the discretion of the Ministry Foul Brood Officer. In some cases the 'cure' has turned out to be just as fatal as the disease.

TROUBLES AFFECTING ADULT BEES
Acarine Disease

The signs are masses of 'crawlers' outside the hive, on the ground or on stems of nearby plants, with distended abdomens and fluttering wings which appear to be dislocated — the front and rear wings separated. The cause is an infestation of mites into the breathing tubes (tracheae) which breed and multiply, and suck the blood of their hosts through the walls of the trachea. The mites can only enter the spiracles of young bees not more than five to six days old but can spread rapidly. There are two main methods of treatment:

1. During late autumn or early spring, by inserting into the hive an absorbent pad moistened with carefully measured doses of 'Frow' mixture. The fumes destroy the mites but there may also be loss of bees with damaged tracheae.
2. By burning strips of 'Folbex', which are impregnated with an acaricide, in an empty super above the combs. This is best done in warm weather in early summer as it is not effective in cool weather. The smoke kills the mites but seems to have no bad effects on the brood, queen or stored pollen and honey.

Both Frow mixture and Folbex strips can be had from Bee Diseases Insurance Ltd. (see Appendix 2) or from your local association. Full instructions as to use are given with the packs.

Nosema

The cause is a microscopic organism – a protozoan – which lives and multiplies in the digestive cells of the bee's midgut. Symptoms are splashes of excreta on the combs and hive body, a heap of dead or moribund bees outside the hive and a general dwindling in strength especially in spring. The disease tends to flare up in adverse, damp conditions and then die down again. Many experienced beekeepers believe it to be endemic and extra stress or disturbance may trigger off a bout.

Treatment is to feed an antibiotic, fumagillin, in the autumn with a syrup feed and this treatment is often given as a prophylactic. The earliest possible opportunity should be taken to get the bees on to clean comb and to disinfect the frames. The old combs *can* be disinfected but it is safer to cut out the wax and replace with fresh foundation – after the frames have been sterilized, of course.

The disinfecting agent is the fumes of acetic acid. Stack boxes of suspect frames and/or combs on a floor board somewhere sheltered but not in a totally enclosed space, and insert a pad soaked in 80 per cent acetic acid. Stuff the entrance with an old piece of sacking and cover the top with a well-fitting hive roof or other covering. The fumes will kill the nosema spores but are very corrosive. Metal objects such as metal ends are attacked by the acid fumes so should be removed first. Handle the acid with the greatest care and immediately wash off any splashes on your skin.

Leave for a week undisturbed. Combs fumigated in this way must be aired for a minimum of forty-eight hours before re-use.

Amoeba Disease

Amoeba disease is caused by another microscopic protozoan which lives and thrives in the bees' excretory organs (Malpigian tubules). The bees usually exhibit no marked symptoms but do not seem to 'do well'. An attack often passes unnoticed until diagnosis by microscopic examination.

Bee Paralysis

This is a virus disease affecting adult bees. There are many trembling 'crawlers' who find it difficult, if not impossible, to fly. The disease is frequently present along with other adult diseases and may pass unidentified. The combination is likely to prove fatal to the colony. Re-queening with a young and vigorous queen usually effects a cure.

Dysentery

Dysentery is not a disease but a condition which may arise when bees are confined to the hive for long periods and/or have unsuitable winter stores. Normally, bees can retain their faeces for some time until a spell of fine weather; even an hour or so enables them to take a cleansing flight. There is some evidence that there is a water recycling process in the abdomen which helps to reduce the bulk withheld in the rectum.

However, if confinement continues, there inevitably comes the point when the bees will be compelled to defaecate within the hive — something that they intensely dislike doing. The faecal splashes are good breeding grounds for any disease organisms present. Do not mistake these signs for indications of nosema unless other clinical symptoms are also present.

Waxmoth

The waxmoth will ruin stored combs. The female moth lays her eggs in old comb — particularly old brood comb with accumulated cocoons — and the hatched larvae eat their way through the comb leaving a horrible mess of tunnels and tangled silk fibres.

As a preventive, stack your supers for the winter interleaved with sheets of newspaper and give each storey a generous sprinkling of para-di-chlor-benzine crystals (PDB, obtainable at chemists). The moths dislike the smell and will leave the combs alone. Air the combs before using them next year.

Invasions of Animals and Birds

Mice will get into hives as soon as the weather turns frosty. Before this happens, fit mouseguards over entrances. These are strips of metal perforated with $\frac{1}{4}$ inch (6mm) holes. Bees can come and go freely but the mice will be kept out. You can make your own from strips of perforated zinc the full length of the entrance with a slot cut about 3 inches (7.5cm) long and not more than $\frac{1}{4}$ inch (6mm) high. If you have made your roofs fit badly, mice will also get in above the inner cover and make a nice warm nest by chewing up any pieces of carpet or sacking you have laid on the inner cover. The remedy is clear.

Woodpeckers can be a nuisance in rural situations. They will rapidly drill a hole through the wall of a hive and make a good meal of your larvae. These beautiful birds are difficult to discourage but if you get a visitation, try strips of polythene fastened with drawing pins to the roof and hanging down over the walls. This will tend to put them off though it will make your hives look a little unsightly.

Cows and horses love to lean on and rub themselves against any hives sited in their meadows. The hives invariably come off worst so if you are lucky enough to have an apiary at a farm you must arrange some kind of strong fence to keep the stock off.

Pesticides

Poison spray, either used as pesticides or herbicides, causes the death of many, many thousands of bees annually. Bees can be caught in the spray either on a crop whose blossom they are working or, quite often, while they are overflying an area in which they are not interested but which is on their flight path home. If the spray is an insecticide lethal to bees they may never reach home. But some insecticides are slow acting, and herbicides are not actually lethal to bees. When bees carry these sprays back to the hive, the result is often catastrophic. The guard bees reject the homecomers because of their strange odour. Fighting occurs on a massive scale and dead bees, literally by the bucketful, will be found on the ground outside the hive. The colony may well lose so many foragers that the possibility of a honey surplus for the year will be nil. The weakened colony may need feeding and careful nursing back to full strength.

Attempts at early warning schemes have been tried but with minimal success, I think. Three courses seem open to the beekeeper:
1. To do nothing and 'hope for the best'.
2. To move his bees at least two miles away to another site temporarily, and then bring them back when all danger is past.
3. Shut his bees in before spraying starts and release them only when any liquid spray has dried.

To move bees may not be a practical possibility. There may be no alternative site available. The warning of impending spraying may not be received in time. Because of conditions of his work, the beekeeper may not be able to act at the required time.

Bees shut up in warm weather will suffer considerable distress and losses — perhaps very considerable if the weather is hot. If gauze is pinned over the entrance they will fight to get out, die and block the ventilating gauze, thus defeating its object. The temperature inside can easily rise to such an extent that wax will melt and combs collapse.

If you *have* to shut in your bees, the following may help to tide them over for twenty-four hours or so if the weather is not excessively hot, but confinement will still be a chancy business.

1. Place an empty super or brood box on the floor board below the brood chamber and another on top of the top super.
2. Put a contact feeder filled with water in the top empty super resting on the top bars.
3. Cover the top empty super with a wire gauze screen instead of the inner cover.
4. Block the entrance completely with a thick piece of plastic foam.

Growers and spray contractors could do much to mitigate the problem. Most of them go in for 'overkill' anyway. Fewer bees are flying before 8 a.m. or after 8 p.m. than at midday so it would seem sensible to spray early or late. Late evening is best as it gives an overnight interval for the spray to dry out before bees are on the move again. There are often long cool, cloudy periods when bee foraging is at a minimum.

Aerial spraying from fixed wing aircraft is more hazardous to bees, other livestock and humans than by tractor or helicopter. Far too often there are considerable areas contaminated by drifting spray. Bees work open blossom and this is when the crop is most likely to be improved by efficient pollination — spraying should *never* be carried out on open blossom.

Granular forms of insecticides are less harmful to bees and other beneficial insects than wet sprays, although it must be said that granular insecticides are not effective on all crops.

Some insecticides are less harmful to bees than others. Pirimicarb is one of the least harmful and has the added advantage of leaving aphid predators unharmed.

Oilseed rape presents a difficult problem. The crop suffers much from the depredations of blossom beetle and seed weevil, and the experts hold that only spraying on open blossom is effective. The blossoms yield nectar copiously and are avidly worked by bees. However, even here there is a partial solution. Perimeter spraying, leaving the centre of the crop unsprayed will do much to control the pests which penetrate the fields of growing rape from their winter quarters in the surrounding hedgerows.

If you feel compelled to spray your own garden flowers and crops:
1. Read the instructions on the label.
2. Avoid spraying in windy weather.
3. Adhere strictly to the instructions as to dilutions. *Never* add 'just another drop or two for luck'.

Household slow release insecticides are worth a mention. Many people use them in the house and in outbuildings against the house fly and blow fly, and very effective they are too. Sadly there have been a number of cases where beekeepers have stored combs and wax foundation in rooms with these slow release units. The active insecticidal element is readily absorbed by wax and remains there for a very long time indeed, gradually being released by rising temperatures. The inside of a hive is just about right for this re-activation. Never store wax or combs near slow release units. Incidentally, they seem to be much more effective against flies and bees than they are against wasps, although curiously enough, some aerosol fly sprays will knock down wasps immediately but do not seem to affect bees a great deal.

Sugars in Lime Nectar

When limes are in flower it is not altogether uncommon, especially in hot, dry seasons, to find masses of bees lying underneath the trees, dead, paralysed or apparently 'drunk'. There are often more bumbles than honeybees, and people become concerned at the losses.

The trouble arises from certain complex sugars in lime nectar which are abnormally high in dry weather. The chief culprit is mannose. This is a common sugar which can safely be utilized by the digestive system of man, but which upsets the metabolism of certain species of bee. The bees lack the enzyme which can complete the breakdown of the mannose into assimilable compounds and toxic sugars collect in the blood and thorax. The thoracic flight and leg muscles are unable to function and affected bees exhibit all the symptoms of paralysis.

Not all lime trees produce the toxic sugars; the worst are *Tilia petiolaris* and *Tilia cordata*.

Sometimes, but fortunately not often, the honeydew produced on the leaves of lime trees can be toxic to honeybees. In this case, the offending sugar is melezitose. The effects are as described above.

APPENDIX

Development of Brood in days

	Queen	Worker	Drone
Egg	3	3	3
Larvae	5	5	6
Capped	8	13	15
Total days from egg to emergence	16	21	24
Possible life span	3-4 years	6-26 weeks	a season
Age at first flight	2-8 days	4 days	14 days

Normal Division of Labour According to Age (N.B. These times may be varied due to exceptional conditions in the colony.)

1-3 days old	Clean and polish cell walls
3-6 days old	Feed older brood
6-10 days old	Feed younger brood
8-12 days old	Feed and tend queen
11-18 days old	House cleaning
12-18 days old	Wax-making and comb building
18-20 days old	Guard duties
20 days old and after	Foraging for nectar, pollen, water and propolis.

Honey Values

Energy value: 1,290 calories per lb.
Compared with: 1,200 for eggs, 1,280 for bread, 1,150 for lean meat.
1 lb honey has a calorific value equal to 30 eggs, 6 pints (2.3 litres) milk, 8 lb (3.6kg) plums, 10 lb (4.5kg) green peas, 12 lb (5.4kg) apples, 20 lb (9kg) carrots.

Colours of Pollen Loads

White: bluebell, heather.
Greenish white: currant, gooseberry, raspberry, blackberry.
Greenish yellow: clover, apple, lime, willow.
Yellow-green: privet, elm, arabis.

Light yellow: birch, hazel, plum, mustard, tulip.
Golden yellow: berberis, coltsfoot, daffodil, dahlia, dandelion, ragwort
Orange: anchusa, broom, celandine, crocus, gorse, hollyhock.
Reddish-brown: mignonette, sanfoin.
Crimson: horse chestnut, London Pride.
Dark purple (almost black): poppy.
Blue: purple loosestrife, rose bay willow herb.

SUGGESTED FURTHER READING

The Art of Beekeeping, W. Hamilton, (Herald Press, York)
A Manual of Beekeeping, E.B. Wedmore (BBNO, Jasmin Cottage, Steventon, Basingstoke, Hampshire)
The Complete Handbook of Beekeeping, H. Mace, (Ward Lock Ltd.)

Ministry of Agriculture Bulletins
No. 9 *Beekeeping*
No. 100 *Diseases of Bees*
No. 206 *Swarming of Bees*

Ministry of Agriculture Advistory Leaflets (single copies free):
No. 328 *Importance of Bees in Orchards*
No. 344 *Migratory Beekeeping*
No. 574 *Making Increase*
No. 347 *Beeswax from the Apiary*
No. 306 *Foul Brood*
No. 330 *Acarine*
Bo. 362 *Examination of Bees for Acarine*
No. 561 *Brood Diseases and Disorders*

Journals
Bee Craft (monthly), The Secretary, 15 West Way, Copthorne Bank, Crawley, Sussex.
British Bee Journal (monthly), 46 Queen Street, Geddington, Kettering, Northamptonshire.

USEFUL ADDRESSES

(It is courteous to send a stamped addressed envelope when asking for information – it speeds a reply too!)

The British Beekeepers Association: The Secretary, 55 Chipstead Lane, Sevenoaks, Kent, TN13 2AJ.

The International Bee Research Association: The Secretary, Hill House, Chalfont St Peter, Buckinghamshire, SL9 0NR.

The National Beekeeping Specialist, Luddington Experimental Horticulture Station, Stratford-on-Avon, Warwickshire, CV37 9SJ.

The Beekeeping Advisor, ADAS, Trawscoed, Aberystwyth, Dyfed.

Appliance Manufacturers

Robert Lee Ltd., Beehive Works, George Street, Uxbridge, Middlesex.

Steele and Brodie Ltd., Wormit, Fife, Scotland.

E.H. Taylor Ltd., Beehive Works, Welwyn, Hertfordshire, AL6 0AZ.

E.H. Thorne (Beehives) Ltd., Beehive Works, Wragby, Lincolnshire, LN3 5LA.

Ministry of Agriculture, Fisheries and Food (Publications), Tolcarne Drive, Pinner, Middlesex, HA5 2DT.

National Honey Show: The Secretary, 14 Southgate, Beaminster, Dorset.

Bee Diseases Insurance Ltd.: The Secretary, Valley's End, Weare Giffard, Bideford, Devon.

The National Beekeeping Centre, Stoneleigh Park, Kenilworth, Warwickshire.

Samples of bees for examination for suspected disease should be packed in a matchbox (about 30 bees) and sent to The National Beekeeping Specialist at Luddington or, if you live in Wales, to the Beekeeping Advisor at Trawscoed. Addresses as above.

INDEX